A LIFE FORCE IN LIFE SCIENCE: DISCOVERING IDA MACLEAN

A LIFE FORCE IN LIFE SCIENCE

DISCOVERING IDA MACLEAN

Penny Freedman

The Book Guild Ltd

First published in Great Britain in 2020 by

The Book Guild Ltd
9 Priory Business Park
Wistow Road, Kibworth
Leicestershire, LE8 0RX
Freephone: 0800 999 2982
www.bookguild.co.uk
Email: info@bookguild.co.uk
Twitter: @bookguild

Typeset in 12pt Adobe Jensen Pro

Printed and bound by CPI Group (UK) Ltd, Croydon, CR0 4YY

ISBN 978 191320 832 5

British Library Cataloguing in Publication Data.
A catalogue record for this book is available from the British Library.

For Robert,
remembering happiness

Robert Freedman
2nd January 1946 – 17th October 2017

CONTENTS

Acknowledgements

My thanks to the Leverhulme Trust for generous research funding, to Dr Vicky Long, who found invaluable material on Ida Smedley-MacLean and her contemporaries, to Dr Stephen Soanes at the University of Warwick for his contribution to the research, to Professor Hilary Marland for her unfailing support of the research, to Dr Grace Brockington for introducing us to Barbara MacLean's memoir and leading us to Ida's diaries, and to Frank Hatt for the text of his play about Constance Smedley. My personal thanks to Dr Patricia Fara for her enthusiastic support and forthright advice, and her student Will Peck for access to his excellent MA dissertation, to Mary Wells (Dr Mary Harrison) for countless hours transcribing the diaries and listening to me talk, to Judy Klinkenberg for checking for scientific blunders, to Genny Freedman for her invaluable work on the photographs, and to Anne and John Shneerson for the loan of the diaries which are the beginning and end of this book. My thanks, of course, to my husband, Robert Freedman, who brought this project into our lives and who did an enormous amount of preparatory work from which I have benefited. And I should probably thank too the nameless and countless people whom I have collared to talk at length about my obsession with a remarkable woman.

A Word on Appendices

I HAVE TRIED HERE TO GIVE FULL VALUE TO IDA Smedley-MacLean's scientific work without interrupting the flow of the narrative. To that end, I have described in general terms what she was working on at different periods in her career and given the details of her publications in an appendix. In other appendices, I have included part of the text of a talk given in Prague in 2016, and the obituary written by Ida Smedley-MacLean's co-researcher Dr Leslie Nunn in *Nature*, both of which give detailed accounts of the nature and significance of the scientific work.

A Note on Names

IT HAS BEEN DIFFICULT TO DECIDE WHAT TO CALL Ida Smedley-MacLean in telling her story. The convention is to refer to the subject of a biography by their surname, but 'Smedley-MacLean' is cumbersome and, anyway, that was her work name only. People were not quite sure how to address her in life – they wandered between 'Smedley', 'Smedley-MacLean' and 'MacLean', and between 'Miss', 'Mrs' and 'Dr'. So, I have chosen to refer to her as 'Ida', and if that feels too cosy, I can say in my defence that her family – parents, siblings and husband – usually called her 'Di', so I am making no claim to be part of her inner circle.

As for other names, as far as possible I use the form that Ida uses in her diaries. So, I use first names for her family, first name and surname for friends and some close colleagues, and surnames alone or with titles for others. She lived in a far more formal time than ours, and lifelong colleagues still appear formally in the diaries: Chaim Weizmann, whom she knew for forty years, remained 'Dr Weizmann' to the end although his wife was 'Vera', and her friend, colleague and co-campaigner, Martha Whiteley, was 'Dr Whiteley'. I think I have been consistent.

PREFACE

WHERE ARE THE WOMEN?

1911–2011

IN 1911, A GROUP OF DISTINGUISHED SCIENTISTS IN the new field of biochemistry met in London to set up the Biochemical Society. How typical it is of the confidence of Britain at the time that they felt no need to specify that this was a British organisation: it was simply the Biochemical Society, and the world could beat a path to its door.

Twenty-one years later, the founding members marked the anniversary with a team photograph. A distinguished group it was, including two Nobel prize winners and the directors of several outstanding research institutes. Between them they boasted an impressive display of wing collars, waistcoats, watch chains and luxuriant walrus moustaches. In 2011, my husband, Robert Freedman, a former chair of the Biochemical Society, was asked to take part in its centenary celebrations. A lifelong champion, supporter and mentor of women's careers in biochemistry, he looked at the photograph of the 1932 gathering and asked the question, *Where are the women?* What followed took him on a quest which revealed a group of remarkable, pioneering women, born in the reign of Queen Victoria, who found their way, often by indirect and unpromising routes, into work in biochemistry at its very dawn as a scientific discipline, and none more impressive than the extraordinary Dr Ida Smedley-MacLean, born in Birmingham in 1877.

Ida Smedley, later, professionally, Smedley-MacLean, was an acknowledged star: from her school days onwards, she was a winner of prizes – often the first woman to achieve these awards – and her career was studded with other 'firsts' – the first woman to be appointed to the chemistry department at Manchester University, the first on the executive board of the Biochemical Society, and of the Chemical Society, and the first to chair the Biochemical Society. From the time when she won the highly prestigious Beit Memorial Research Fellowship, she was described in newspapers both at home and abroad as 'Britain's Marie Curie'. She worked for thirty years at the Lister Institute of Preventive Medicine in London, becoming an acknowledged expert on the metabolism of fats and the implications of dietary fat-deficiency. She made her way into all-male worlds and, at the same time, she created female networks to support other women: she founded the British Federation of University Women to campaign for the recognition and rights of women in the professions, was instrumental in the creation of the International Federation of University Women and, for many years, ran the Lyceum clubs – women's social and residential clubs on the model of men's clubs. At the same time, she had a successful marriage; was devoted to her children; and supported her parents, her siblings, and her nephews and nieces. And it was, perhaps, because she spread her energies so widely – because, though she loved her work, she was not obsessive about it – that her potential to be another Marie Curie was not realised in a Nobel prize and public recognition. She did, at times, generate 'the Marie Curie effect' whereby an exceptional woman is taken as the standard by which all other women in her field are judged and found wanting, but she herself would have been mortified to think that she was having such an effect. She enjoyed her successes but she never sought to pull the ladder up after her; she celebrated other women's achievements, enjoyed meeting successful women and campaigned throughout her life for better opportunities for professional women.

Ida, as we soon called her, became a part of our lives when Dr Grace Brockington put Robert in contact with Ida's granddaughter, Dr Anne Shneerson, who offered him access to boxes of diaries and papers left by her grandmother and stored in her attic. The boxes of documents, when we collected them, were astounding – they contained a complete life. Ida, it turned out, had been a compulsive memorialiser, a collector and keeper of the data of her life – photographs, programmes, menus, invitations, news cuttings, telegrams, letters, postcards, dance cards and calling cards – as well as being a diarist. Her remarkable, busy, energetic, loving, productive life was laid out for us.

Robert was not well. He had been diagnosed with an aggressive cancer and the Ida project turned out to be a godsend, both in the good times and the bad that followed. Ida was a third person in our lives, as though a good friend was constantly sharing her life with us on Facebook. I knew about her problems and pleasures with her family, about successes and frustrations at work, about holidays and work trips, campaigns, committee meetings and conferences, shopping, school sports days, games of golf, dinners, concerts and theatre-going – so much theatre-going. Theatre addicts ourselves, we loved reading her comments on the latest London shows and were delighted to discover that she had actually done some professional acting at the same time as she was establishing her scientific career.

In his bid for a small research grant from the Leverhulme Trust, Robert described the intended outcomes of his research as articles, conference papers and – possibly – a book. He wrote the articles, and he presented the papers, at conferences in Seville and Prague. His last paper was in 2016, when he was feeling well and enjoyed a week in Prague, accompanied by our daughter, Zoë, and her partner, Michael, giving a paper at a conference of the European Society for the History of Science. I am not sure that he believed that he would have time to write the book, or that he would have been completely delighted to know that I would do it, but after his death, confronted by the boxes of documents that filled his study, I decided to see what I could do.

My academic background is in the interpretation of texts, so I approached the diaries and memorabilia as a collection of complex texts to be mined for clues to a remarkable life. I went off at tangents too – to read the books Ida was reading and to watch the films she saw. She was not a self-revealing diarist – she only rarely said how she felt, and then very briefly. Often she recorded bare dates and deeds. I had to imagine how she felt from what she did. Faced with a crisis, she didn't lament her lot but simply recorded how she dealt with it. That was her character and I admired it, but it did not make my task easy. In the end, though, I found the omissions as intriguing as the entries. Small puzzles and mysteries abound, but that is what made the writing so interesting.

This is a story that deserves to be told. It is not a noisy story – it does not speak of huge struggles or public triumphs: her research work made a significant contribution to scientific knowledge, but she was not Marie Curie; her resolute campaigning made a difference to the lives of many women, but she was not Emmeline Pankhurst. What made her remarkable was her belief, in the early years of the twentieth century, that she was not constrained by being a woman, that she did not have to make either/or choices, that if she was prepared to work hard enough she could have it all. She was, in fact, inventing for herself the role of the professional working mother.

So, it is a quiet story – a woman's story: the life of a woman of brains, charm, talent, a social conscience, dogged determination, family love and loyalty, unflagging energy; and an exuberant zest for work, friends, music, theatre, sport, travel, clothes, and food. Shattering some glass ceilings along the way, she invented for herself a life which balanced work, public life and motherhood; supported her parents, her siblings and her children; and, when her husband was struck down by a debilitating illness that lasted for several years, she somehow managed to care for him without neglecting any of her other commitments. And she still found time to write her diary. She was, as one awed contemporary put it, 'little less than heroic'.

I have, whenever possible, told her story as she tells it – I wanted my readers to hear her voice. It is a remarkably modern voice, and remarkably young, even in the later diaries. I hope my readers will be willing to go with me into the diaries, to sift through the photographs and letters, to puzzle over inconsistencies and wonder how to fill in the gaps. What follows is an exploration and a journey.

CHAPTER ONE

PRINCESS IDA

1877–1896

FOR THE MOST PART, OUR GIVEN NAMES SAY MORE about our parents than they do about us. They speak of the fashions of our parents' youth, of their family ties, their cultural and class identification, and, most importantly, of their aspirations and hopes for us. William and Anne Smedley named their second daughter Ida. Since this has never been a common name in England and was not a family name either for the Smedleys or for Anne's family, the Duckworths, my guess is that Ida's mother, who had clear and determined aspirations for her daughters, named her younger girl after the heroine of Tennyson's epic poem *The Princess*, published in 1847. In the poem, the beautiful Princess Ida refuses to marry the prince who loves her, and chooses instead to found a university for women, from which men are excluded. The prince and two of his friends get into the college disguised as women. They are found out and are challenged to a battle by Ida's protective brothers. They are wounded in the fighting and lose the battle but are nursed back to health by the women, who, in the process, fall in love with them. Eventually, the princess agrees to marry the prince, on the basis of 'equality in love', and the prince expresses the wish that, in future, 'the man may be more of woman, she of man'.

Tennyson had the best of intentions in writing the poem; he was strongly committed to the higher education of women and may well have been inspired to write the poem by the opening, that year, of Queen's College, London, the first university college for women in the UK. Telling the story from the point of view sometimes of the men, sometimes of the women, he attempted a subtle exploration of the issues – setting women's desire for and right to learning, and knowledge against the pull of love and marriage and family. As a result, he pleased no-one. Proponents of women's education were angered by the way their message was diluted by the romantic elements, while traditionalists found it outrageous. Nearly forty years later, Gilbert and Sullivan found ready audiences for their travesty, *Princess Ida*, which was first performed in 1884. Those masters of the banal and celebrators of entrenched, conservative attitudes took Tennyson's story as an opportunity to mock the whole idea of university study for women, and to add educated women to their gallery of ludicrous types, alongside funny foreigners, absurd poets and monstrous middle-aged women.

But Anne Smedley could afford to ignore this sort of reactionary mockery. Just a year before *Princess Ida* opened at the Savoy Theatre in London, up in Birmingham – their home city, England's thriving industrial heartland and an expanding cultural beacon – a group of young teachers had established exactly the school she was seeking for her girls: King Edward VI High School for Girls, a school which would quickly become the best girls' school in the country for science teaching. The headmistress had been among the first five students to study at Newnham College, Cambridge, founded for women in 1871, and she recruited other Newnham alumnae to teach at the school, three of them outstanding science teachers. In the photograph below of the headmistress and staff of the school, taken in 1884, just after it was founded, the staff look, at first glance, less than inspirational: the severe hairstyles, the solemn faces, the unflattering pie frill collars invite the derogatory label, *'schoolmarms'*. But look again and you notice the three young women who are sitting on the ground: the relaxed posture of one of them, the confident gaze of another, and the fashionable attire of the third – Miss Perry – who sits between the others wearing a daringly low neckline and the most elegant of leg o' mutton sleeves. We see a group of women who are comfortable in themselves and with one another, teachers who would open minds and reveal

Head and staff of King Edward VI High School for Girls, Birmingham, 1884

treasures. I am reminded of the motto of my own school, founded in 1874: *'Knowledge is now no more a fountain sealed'.*

Ida and Constance, her sister, just a year older, started at the school in 1886, when Ida was nine. Before that, they had been taught at home by their mother, who had herself had a good education, including a spell at a finishing school in France. Both girls flourished at the school: Connie embraced the arts, and went on to study at Birmingham School of Art; and Ida thrived on the first-class science teaching, winning one of the school's scholarships, as well as enjoying the musical life and taking leads in school plays (there is a photograph of her, too blurred to be reproduced, in the unlikely role of Shylock!). Here, I think, were the beginnings of her instinctive building of the female networks through which she would operate, successfully and happily, throughout her career. She made two lifelong friends, who were themselves pioneers in the scientific world: Winifred Cullis, who became the first woman professor of medicine in the UK; and Beatrice Thomas, who taught chemistry at Girton College, Cambridge for many years. The three of them were in a favoured group for whom an arrangement was made to attend physiology lectures at a local men's college. Here, at fifteen, Ida met the first of the succession of closed doors that she would encounter and, eventually, stroll through. There were objections from the college staff, and even a threat of resignation from one if *'those little girls from the High School'* came into his lab, but the little girls were not to be deflected, and in the end nobody resigned – an early lesson in keeping their nerve for the future pioneers.

The Smedley children's education was not confined to school. Home life was extraordinarily rich and stimulating. The Smedleys loved involving their children in their own pursuits. They took them to the theatre and to concerts (the earliest dated piece of memorabilia in Ida's archive is a programme for a Paderewski concert at Birmingham Town Hall, kept by the fifteen-year-old). Connie and Ida played the violin and the piano, sang, and acted plays they wrote themselves. Though we might assume that it was Anne Smedley who took responsibility for her daughters' education, it is clear that their father contributed, too. Starting his working life as an accountant, he went on to become chairman of several businesses in Birmingham, including Roneo, one of the first firms to develop new technologies in copying. He was an enthusiast for music and a passionate Shakespeare lover, and used his money to support the arts in the city. As the children were growing up, their father knew most of the great and good in Birmingham, and their mother held what were described as 'salons', to which literary and musical figures were invited. When Connie, Ida and their younger brother, Billy, were old enough, they joined these parties, conversing comfortably with the distinguished guests. They may have seemed horribly precocious to some with traditional views of the place of children, but all three of them, though they went in very different directions, entered adult life with confidence, ease and charm.

It must have been a remarkably happy family life. Ida's closeness to her parents is demonstrated in letters between them in her adult life – easy, informal, affectionate letters, which do not speak of a conventional Victorian upbringing – and Ida and Connie remained close for most of their lives, with Ida not, apparently, resenting the financial and other calls that Connie made on her. When Billy went off the rails, it was to Ida that he turned. Those childhood years of stability and happiness were a bedrock on which she fixed her self-belief, her sense of responsibility, her care for her siblings, and they were the model on which she based her family life with her own children later on.

CHAPTER TWO

AND NOT ALL ARE GENTLEMEN

1896–1899

When Ida was applying for a place at Cambridge, the university had just two women's colleges. One was Girton, founded in 1869, and the other Newnham, founded two years later. Girton is a somewhat forbidding building, turreted like a mediaeval castle, sitting austerely beyond the outskirts of the city, more than two miles from the centre; whereas Newnham, just a ten-minute walk from the city centre, looks like a large and comfortable country house and was designed with domestic spaces for a sense of home. Ida chose Newnham and added to her home comforts by taking her dog, Warwick, with her. It was an eccentric thing to do. He was not allowed to live in the college, of course, but she found a family with whom she could board him out and was able to visit him and take him for walks. It is an early example of her conviction that she did not have to do what was expected and did not have to make binary choices; with initiative and energy (and some money), she could have the best of both worlds.

The photograph overleaf of Ida's room in her final

At Newnham

Ida's college room

year shows a comfortable room with which care has been taken: framed prints and family photographs on the walls; flourishing plants in pots; a handsome desk, centre stage; with well-filled bookcases; and a mantelpiece thick with invitations and cards. It is a room for studying in but also for relaxing and entertaining friends.

In the twenty-five years between the founding of the women's colleges and Ida's arrival at Newnham, the two women's colleges had had to fight inch by inch for the integration of their students into the university. (The term that the establishment liked to use for the women students was 'guests' at the university.) The colleges had first to fight for their students' right to attend lectures – initially their attendance was subject to the agreement of the lecturer – and then for their right to sit examinations, and to have them

Ida outside Newnham College, 1899

marked and be given a degree class. In Ida's time, women science students were still not allowed to take practical classes in the university laboratories; they were confined to their own college laboratories, which were less well equipped, with poorer facilities.

The big public drama of Ida's time at Cambridge was the campaign for women to be allowed to graduate formally and take degrees. As things stood, they did everything that the men did – studied, took exams, were allocated degree classes – but did not leave the university as graduates. Here was where the male establishment drew the line. On 21ˢᵗ May 1897, the dons of Girton and Newnham put forward a proposal, to be voted on by the congregation of the university, that women students be allowed to graduate. The campaign in the run-up to the vote was ferocious: the women undergraduates called on reason and justice; the men responded with cartoons, rude rhymes and solemn invocations of the age-old traditions of the university (reduced to its basics, their argument was that the university was theirs and they might have been prepared to share it if the women had been more attractive). A vote in the congregation meant that anyone with a Cambridge MA could vote on the question, and vote they did, travelling in from the shires – parsons, for the most part, with some lawyers and schoolmasters and a sprinkling of MPs – to put the upstart women back in their place. The motion was heavily defeated by 1,713 to 662. Since this was Cambridge and even *ayes* and *noes* were not archaic enough, the votes were given in Latin as *placets* (it pleases) and *non placets*, enabling jokes about whether the women were pleasing or not.

The solemn thundering of the university newspaper to the effect that the vote had been a triumph in preserving the integrity of the university and defending its status as a serious place of learning was rather undermined by the celebrations of the male undergraduates after the result was announced. They got drunk, threw flour bags in the city centre, let off fireworks and did hundreds of pounds' worth of damage. They hanged an effigy of a woman student and threw missiles at it, then cut it down, beheaded it and carried the pieces to Newnham, where they broke down the gates and scattered the pieces of the effigy in the grounds. A journalist who made his way to Newnham to ask the lecturers there how they felt about the men's behaviour was given a weary smile. '*After all, they are but boys,*' was the comment, '*and not all of them are gentlemen.*' A cool put-down under the circumstances.

The university newspaper's final comment on the affair

was to suggest that the obvious answer to the problem was separate women's universities run by women for women, granting their own degrees, leaving the great universities the all-male preserves they were intended to be – what one might call the Saudi Arabian solution, in fact. It is worth a reminder, at this point, that several colleges of London University were offering degrees to women at this stage, that Oxford granted women degrees in 1920, and Cambridge not until 1947.

Viewing up close the undisguised contempt and misogyny of the male undergraduates in the run-up to the vote and their crude triumphalism afterwards threatened to reduce me to tears of rage, but Ida was probably made of steelier stuff. She kept all the evidence, though, among her papers – every newspaper article, every cartoon, every insulting rhyme – a reminder, if she needed it, of the hurdles that lay ahead.

There are no diaries for Ida's time at Cambridge, but she kept an abundance of mementos of her student years which show how enthusiastically she threw herself into all aspects of university life, despite the efforts of many of the men to make the women students feel like outsiders. She embraced drama, music, sport and social activities, a participant when she could be and a spectator when she could not. Inevitably, much of her social life was within the college, and Ida sang in the choir, played the piano at concerts and took part in college plays. There is a photo, very faded, of her in a production in the college garden. Slim, blonde and dressed in white, she was clearly playing an ingenue role, but this was not the sort of part she really enjoyed – her favourite role was as the formidable Lady Catherine de Bourgh in an adaptation of *Pride and Prejudice*. There is a collection of little printed notes among her memorabilia which show that she was active, too, in a college society. The members met in one another's rooms for discussions and play-readings (earnest young women that they were, they met at ten o'clock in the evening, after the library closed), and they took themselves quite seriously, electing a president and an Hon. Sec., and wearing badges. Ida would spend her adult life establishing and running women's organisations; perhaps this one, formed in the face of exclusion and hostility, was the prototype.

However, she certainly enjoyed a social life outside the college as well. She told her daughter, Barbara, that she was *'never short of admirers'*, and the photos and programmes of balls and dance cards bear this out. She was invited to a performance given by the Footlights, a recently established revue group, an off-shoot of the university dramatic society. Women students could not perform, of course – when women were needed, professional actresses were hired – but Ida and others were invited to a ladies' night, where suitably dainty refreshments (cucumber, shrimp and anchovy sandwiches, and raspberry and vanilla wafers) were served. Ida kept a photo of the company, posed in self-consciously thespian style. She also kept a professionally produced photo of the university boat race crew. The men are formally dressed, in high collars and dark ties, hair and moustaches immaculate. Great care has been taken to present them in as flattering a light as possible. They do look like the lords of creation.

I could not help speculating about possible romantic attachments. Did Ida know a young man in the Footlights? Was she attached to someone in the boat race crew, or was the photo just eye candy? Who took her to the St John's College ball, or the Trinity Boat Club ball? She was an attractive, confident, talented young woman, and it is not hard to believe that she had admirers. The dance cards she kept are full – she had a partner for every dance – but perhaps those were the cards she kept because they represented the pinnacle of social success.

Ida in evening dress

Ida's acting in Cambridge was restricted to college plays, but in the middle of her second year she was summoned back to Birmingham to take the lead in a play of Connie's. Among her memorabilia of her Cambridge years, I found a programme for the inaugural performance of the Edgbaston Dramatic Club in 1898. Edgbaston is the leafy, wealthy area of Birmingham where the Smedleys lived, and this opening performance was clearly a glitzy affair, the new club boasting a list of patrons which included the Countess of Warwick, Lady Newport and Lord Leigh, together with two baronets and four MPs, including Joseph Chamberlain, then Secretary of State for the Colonies and heavily involved in the Boer

War. We might guess that the twenty-two-year-old Connie had persuaded her father to use his connections to secure this patronage, since the first play in the double bill that was put on was *On the Road to Inglefield* by Constance Smedley. It was about Dorothea Jordan, the leading Regency actress, and mistress of William IV, and it was clearly an early version of Connie's play *Mrs Jordan*, which was later put on in the West End with Mrs Patrick Campbell in the title role, launching Connie's writing career. The EDC programme shows that for this first performance the role of Mrs Jordan was played by Ida Smedley. So, Ida was the person Connie trusted for the leading role in this very high-profile debut, and Ida was willing to take time off in the middle of her second year at Cambridge, with Part I Tripos exams only weeks away, to support her sister. No doubt she enjoyed doing it, and she managed to get a first in the Tripos, anyway. As ever, she acted on her belief that, given an either/or choice, if you were prepared to work hard enough you could say, 'Both.'

CHAPTER THREE

EVEN AN AURA OF BOHEMIA

1899–1909

AFTER CAMBRIDGE, FOR THE NEXT FEW YEARS, IDA followed the path familiar today to young scientists looking for an academic career: short-term research posts funded by grants and scholarships and temporary university teaching work. What would have been unfamiliar in England at the turn of the twentieth century was the idea of a young, single, independent, professional woman moving between jobs and cities in pursuit of her career. We encounter single young women living alone in the literature of that period, and the picture is generally discouraging – narrow lives of strained gentility and little comfort, in boarding houses and rented rooms – but Ida's life was not like that. She was now keeping scrapbooks as a form of diary, including photos, programmes, letters and occasional written notes of events. A trawl through these shows that she seems always to have had enough money to enjoy herself. She loved going to conferences, always including a few days' sightseeing along the way; she took trips abroad; she enjoyed theatre- and concert-going; and dinners and lunches out with friends. It was an enviable life, subsidised, I have to assume, by her generous father.

There was a hiatus before Ida found her first research post in 1901 – a gap year, in fact, in which, among other things, she took speech and drama lessons in London and actually got some walk-on parts in West End theatres. The lessons and the stage experience were invaluable later – she was always an exceptionally persuasive, confident and charismatic public speaker. A legend grew up among her scientific colleagues that she had nearly decided to go on the stage instead of continuing in biochemistry. It is hard to know how true this was, but it may be that a stage career was actually a more viable prospect for a young woman in 1901 than a career in biochemistry! Whatever the truth, it is clear that her looks and personality made this seem credible to her contemporaries. Whatever doubts she may have had, she was applying for research scholarships, and in 1901 she won a Bathurst Scholarship and went to work under Henry Armstrong at the Central Technical College (later Imperial College, London). Armstrong was not the obvious man to encourage a young woman to join his research team, as we can see in the photo overleaf. His publicly expressed view, when opposing women's admission to the Chemical Society, was that:

> 'Young women should be withdrawn from the temptation to become absorbed in the work, for fear of sacrificing their womanhood; they are those who should be regarded as chosen people, as destined to be the mothers of future chemists of ability.'[1]

If that was his view, what made him accept the young Miss

---

1   Rayner-Canham, M. and Rayner-Canham, G. *Chemistry Was Their Life* (London: Imperial College Press, 2008) p74.

Smedley into his lab? Was it just that she brought her own funding with her on her scholarship, or was she so exceptional that even he was prepared to put his prejudices aside for once? Ida coped for two years, doing classical organic chemistry, but the photo of the Armstrong group brings home what an odd and isolating experience it must have been, especially after the female companionship of her three years at Newnham (and did Armstrong always look as disdainful as that?).

Ida looks confident enough sitting there among the suits, and she took an enthusiastic part in the life of the college. She kept a programme for a college concert, dated 14th May 1902, at which she accompanied songs on the piano and gave a solo recitation, *A Feminine Diplomatist* – a humorous piece, presumably, about how a woman negotiates her way in a man's world. If so, it must have taken some nerve and some self-

Henry Armstrong's research group

confidence, in that environment, to tackle the issue head-on and make a joke of it.

It is possible that Connie, now well into her writing career and embracing feminist causes, wrote it for her. Connie and Ida were still close. One of the most intriguing items in the scrapbook for 1902 is a telegram sent by Connie, addressed to Ida at work:

> 'Smedley, Technical Institute, Exhibition Road, Kennington Wenwood ill Ida. Come 1.30 Victoria play tonight and Saturday, Connie.'

The telegram was handed in in Canterbury at 12.33. If sent immediately, it could hardly have been delivered to Ida by a boy on a bike before one o'clock, and the instruction was to catch the 1.30 train from Victoria! Whether or not she caught that train, Ida did go. Postcards of Canterbury are stuck into her scrapbook, along with her annotation: '7*th*–9*th* Feb – played the part of Kitty O'Shea in "When the Cat's Away" at the Theatre Royal'. It would have taken at least an hour and a half to get to Canterbury by train, which – even supposing that Ida did drop everything and jumped onto the 1.30 train – would have given her a maximum of four hours to learn and rehearse the role. Had she perhaps played it before? Had Connie put her on stand-by to understudy the unreliable 'Wenwood'? I was frustrated not to know more about this, and about the play itself. I assume that it was about Katharine O'Shea and her decade-long affair with the Irish politician Charles Stewart Parnell, which was used by his enemies to bring his political career to an end in 1890. Katharine O'Shea would have been a character to appeal to the feminist Connie – a woman demonised by the right-wing press, which labelled her with the offensive name *Kitty*, a slang term for a prostitute. So, almost exactly four years after she took a break from Cambridge to launch Connie's play about Dora Jordan, Ida dropped everything again to play another mistress of a powerful man. She had no prissy qualms about playing women of dubious reputation, and was, I assume, good at it.

The rescue mission to Connie in 1902 rather sheds doubt on Connie's comment, in her memoir (titled, with typical bravura, *Crusaders*) that once Ida *'took up Chemistry as her calling our close association naturally ceased'*.[2] Connie adds, rather poignantly, that she found she could no longer play the violin without Ida to accompany her and had to abandon it. Barbara, Ida's daughter, who is very disparaging about Connie in her short family memoir,[3] points out that this is the only mention of Ida by name in Connie's entire memoir. This seems a good place to consider Ida's relationship with her sister.

Connie was barely a year older than Ida, which made them close, but must also have made them rivals – and the rivalry was more on Connie's part. Barbara quotes a rhyme that Connie made up about Ida:

'Now Con had a sister called Ida,
Who looked very paltry beside her,
For Di wasn't pretty
Nor clever nor witty
And so we won't stop to deride her.'

Barbara says she heard the rhyme from Ida, who laughed when she repeated it, but she comments that the fact that her mother remembered it years later suggested that it had sunk deep. The truth was that, as Connie knew, Ida actually was pretty and clever and witty, and she was, moreover, able-

---

2 Smedley, A.C., *Crusaders: Reminiscences* (London: Duckworth, 1929).
3 MacLean, B. *Some Midland Ancestors* (unpublished memoir, 1997).

bodied – tall and sporty – whereas Connie was disabled. She was very lame from early childhood and able to walk only with crutches. Barbara suggests that this may have been the result of polio; Connie wrote in her memoir that she was dropped by a nursemaid and fell down a flight of steps; Barbara says that almost everything that Connie writes in her memoir is untrue! Whatever the reason, it seems that Connie was a sickly child but, encouraged by her parents, had a fierce determination to succeed. The critical Barbara says of her:

> 'My aunt had many gifts and advantages. She was pretty, musical, artistic, vivacious and talented in many ways. She showed dogged courage in surmounting her disabilities. But she was completely self-centred. This tendency was probably fostered by the attention paid to her as a child by her parents to help her overcome her ill-health and, as far as possible, her lameness.'

Whether or not that was Ida's analysis of her sister's character, she seems always to have felt a responsibility to her: rescuing her from difficulties, supporting hare-brained projects and helping her financially throughout her life. Perhaps this relationship was the foundation of her belief that, blessed with good fortune as she was, she had an obligation not just to succeed herself but to help other women to prosper too.

However, in 1902, when she summoned Ida to Canterbury, Connie might have seemed the more successful of the two. While Ida's career in chemistry was still uncertain, Connie was already making a name as a journalist, had been successful in getting her plays put on and was writing a novel, *The April Princess*, which would be very well received. Connie was also ahead of Ida in her commitment to feminism (*feminist*, as a term, had first started to be used in the UK in the 1890s). As a journalist, Connie was braving both verbal and physical abuse by following women's suffrage marches and demonstrations and reporting sympathetically on them. She had also taken the initiative of founding the first Lyceum Club, a club for professional women in London and a parallel to the London men's clubs, providing women with accommodation when working away from home, and the opportunity to find companionship and support with other women. She had persuaded her father to finance the enterprise and there were soon clubs in cities around the country and, eventually, elsewhere in the world. Ida was recruited to the board as their science representative.

While Connie was in the public eye in 1903, Ida was back in Cambridge, back at Newnham. The two-year term of her research scholarship was over, and she had left Henry Armstrong's group to take up a job as a practical demonstrator in the Newnham chemistry teaching laboratory. This was really a step backwards: without a proper academic post, it must have been frustrating not to be able to continue with her research, and her opportunities to meet and discuss with chemists in other colleges must have been limited. However, she was soon back in London for another two years, this time as a research fellow at the Royal Institution. There she was able to complete the work she had started under Henry Armstrong and, in 1905, was awarded the degree of Doctor of Science. This was the standard higher degree for scientists in the UK at the time, PhDs being introduced later to be in line with practice in the USA. Now, as Dr Smedley, she was poised for an academic career, but there were hurdles ahead and she would soon be campaigning for the right to be taken seriously in the world of academic science.

The Chemical Society of London was the professional body for all those working in the field of chemistry – as long as they were male. Women were excluded from membership, but in 1904 the board decided to elect Marie Curie as an honorary foreign member of the Society. Here was *the Curie effect* in essence: she was such a remarkable woman that she could be honoured in this way, but other women who were less exceptional could be ignored. Infuriated, Ida and her friend Martha Whiteley, who was working at Imperial College, combined to canvass their networks of other women chemists – schoolfriends, fellow students, former colleagues and co-workers – in order to raise a petition for the admission of women to the society. The petition noted that in the thirty years from the society's founding in 1873, its journals had published 300 papers by some 150 women authors. The figures made nonsense of the women's exclusion, but the members were obdurate, and the petition still failed.

This campaign may have failed, but she was not ready to give up on the cause, nor on activism in general, when she took up her first real academic post in 1906 at Manchester, where she stayed for four years, teaching and carrying out research on the optical properties of organic compounds. It was, in many ways, an exciting move: she was the first woman on the academic staff of the chemistry department, this was a full-time academic post and she was living independently a long way from home.

As a new lecturer in the chemistry department, she was soon invited to address the student chemical society but turned down the invitation when she found that women students were not allowed to be members of the society – or indeed to go into the student union building where the talks took place. Perhaps it was this, combined with the rebuffs from the Chemical Society, that prompted her next initiative. In March 1907, she convened a meeting, at Manchester High School for Girls, attended by seventeen university and professional

Dr Smedley in the laboratory at Manchester

women, to consider a proposal for establishing a Federation of
University Women, with aims including:

> '...*to work for the removal of sex disabilities, to facilitate
> the communication and co-operation of university women
> and to afford opportunity for the expression of a united
> opinion by university women...*'

Launching the proposal, she was an inspiration to her
audience. One of those attending commented many years
later, '*I remember quite clearly... Miss Smedley, fair-haired and
blue-eyed, held forth vigorously as... she advocated the formation
of a Federation...*'[4]

4   Sondheimer, J. *History of the British Federation of University Women,
    1907–1957* (BFUW, 1957*)*.

Once launched, the BFUW quickly became a remarkably effective networking and lobbying body for working women graduates and for women academics. Within a year, the Manchester Federation had more than fifty members, and plans were being laid to develop similar groupings in other cities and generate a national Federation. Within a further year this was established, with representative groups in Leeds, Liverpool, Sheffield, Birmingham, Bangor and Cardiff, as well as Oxford, Cambridge and London. And Ida drove this development from the beginning, becoming secretary of the nascent organisation and acknowledged as its motivating force. She was in her early thirties, and had confidence and charisma. The official history of the BFUW[5] notes, '*Those who knew her speak of her radiant personality*'. Mentioning her stage connections, it adds that she had the hallmarks of a great actress: '*sensitivity to mood, generosity, impetuosity and even a certain aura of Bohemia*'. The reference to Bohemia, I imagine, alludes to her theatrical and artistic connections, rather than to an unconventional lifestyle – her diaries suggest a thoroughly organised and disciplined woman. (When Robert included this quote in a paper about Ida at a conference in Prague, he realised that he was actually in the old state of Bohemia and had to explain that the reference was cultural rather than geographic.)

The first campaign that the BFUW took up was on behalf of the women completing their medical training who were being barred from applying for resident medical posts at Manchester Royal Infirmary. The justification given by the hospital for the exclusion was the lack of suitable accommodation (excuses for exclusion were nearly always accommodation or lavatories). The effect was to prevent women from completing their

---

5 Sondheimer, J. *History of the British Federation of University Women, 1907–1957* (BFUW, 1957*)*.

medical training. This is exactly the kind of case that Ida must have hoped that the BFUW would tackle – a barrier to women's professional development, maintained through some combination of prejudice and inertia. She went with a deputation to a meeting with the hospital authorities, followed it up with a polite but firm insistence that it could not be impossible to find accommodation, and enlisted the ready support of the *Manchester Guardian* (forerunner of today's *Guardian*). Eventually, at a board meeting of the hospital, a resolution was passed to find the accommodation and to open the posts to women. It was the BFUW's first success, and Ida kept the complete archive – the letters, the resolutions, the news cuttings – as evidence of it.

The continuing battle over the Chemical Society was dispiriting, though, particularly a flurry of activity at the end of 1909 around a meeting of the council of the society to discuss the issue. Ida's diary records a build-up of excitement, discussions with sympathetic men in the society, the day of the meeting and, finally, the bad news from London:

'5ᵗʰ Dec
Heard from Miss Whiteley that the Council are only going to offer us the doubtful privilege of being "paying guests" which of course we shall decline. Hockey match Ashburne & The Oaks v College 2ⁿᵈ'

It was a huge disappointment, but the note about the hockey match (was this a student match, or did she play?) is absolutely characteristic of the woman who emerges from these diaries. On another occasion, after a depressing meeting on the same issue, she went off to coach a student theatre group and then went out to dinner and music with friends – '*a very pleasant evening*'. This is, perhaps, the secret of her success in juggling the three strands of her life later on: science, family and campaigning. She had extraordinary resilience and she could switch from one to another with full commitment. Here, in 1909, the decision of the Chemical Society was dominating her thoughts, and the decision was a blow – especially galling since the leading opponent of women's admission to the society was her own former supervisor – but she could care about a hockey match, take a rehearsal, relax with friends and take pleasure in music. Her political campaigning was determined but not obsessive – not an easy balance to find.

In Manchester, the home of the Pankhursts, it was inevitable that she would be swept up into the women's suffrage movement, now in full swing. She was a passionate suffragist, ready to serve on committees, to organise, to march, to demonstrate, to speak (Miss Ida Smedley DSc had a certain cachet on flyers for meetings). She kept an official, printed programme for 23rd and 24th October 1908 for a Manchester Women's Suffrage Demonstration, along with associated news cuttings, including a *Manchester Guardian* photograph of Manchester University women lining up, in academic dress, to take part in the demonstration. Another item among the suffrage memorabilia for this period is a lady's ticket for a fundraising dance at West Didsbury Public Hall, with a dance card showing that she had a partner for every dance except the last waltz – not as elegant an occasion as a Cambridge May ball, but she was still a social success!

These campaigns took up time and energy, but there was work, too, and work went well. With her personality and communication skills, she must have been an effective teacher; her research went so well that it earnt her a prestigious research fellowship at the end of four years; and she made interesting and influential friends among her colleagues. Contemporaries in the chemistry department included Gertrude Walsh

Robinson, and her husband and collaborator Robert Robinson, one of Britain's most influential natural product chemists. They shared a penchant for working through the night in the lab, became close friends (collectively known as 'the night owls') and continued their friendship throughout their careers. Another colleague was Chaim Weizmann: chemist, industrialist, Zionist and – many years later – the first President of the State of Israel. Ida became a close friend of Weizmann and of his wife, Vera, who was a doctor. Ida's letters to her mother mention them frequently, and when she left Manchester for London, the Weizmanns often came to stay with her on trips to London. One year they even joined the Smedley family for Christmas.

Marie Stopes, a paleo-botanist before she became famous as a proponent of birth control, had arrived at Manchester two years before Ida to join the botany department as the university's first woman lecturer, and was warned on her arrival by the professor of botany that she was '*a risky experiment*'.[6] She told Ida that she had learnt how not to lecture by attending classes given by older men.[7]

Single women – unattached, divorced or widowed – sometimes complain that they are not invited out because they don't come as part of a convenient pair, but Ida's single state seems to have been no hindrance to her social life. The diary entries for this period are full of dinner parties, lunches, At Homes, garden parties, soirées, whist drives and theatre outings, as well as more formal invitations to university receptions in Manchester and Cambridge.

Towards the end of the Manchester scrapbook, there are cuttings of two marriage notices, both from January 1909:

---

6   Maude, A. *The Authorized Life of Marie C. Stopes* (London: Williams and Norgate, 1924) pp55–6. Quoted in Fara, 2018.

7   Ibid.

'SMEDLEY–MOORE on the 18th Jan at the British Consulate, Paris, William Herbert only son of W.T. Smedley of 11 Mecklenburgh Sq WC to Olivia Kate third daughter of Oscar Louis Wood Moore of West Kensington.'

'ARMFIELD–SMEDLEY On the 20th January Maxwell elder son of J.J. Armfield of Ringwood Hants to Constance, elder daughter of W.T. Smedley of 11 Mecklenburgh Sq WC.'

Olive Moore, whom Ida's brother Billy was marrying, was an actress from a theatrical family; Maxwell Armfield, Connie's new husband, had been a fellow student of hers at Birmingham School of Art and became a respected artist. Connie's marriage was a long and happy one; Billy's marriage did not last. Oddly, alongside the cuttings are telegrams addressed to Ida, announcing that the marriages have taken place, so it seems that she was not actually at either wedding. Billy's wedding seems to have been an impulsive affair. Ida saw him several times while she was in London for the Christmas break, without any mention of marriage plans in her diary. Olive was living in Paris with her family, and the decision to marry quickly and quietly and not in England may have been influenced by a need not to overshadow Connie, the family's prima donna, whose wedding was planned for 20th January. Connie's wedding was also a quiet register office event, but Ida kept a newspaper report (possibly written by Connie herself) which gives a long and glowing account of the bride's talents and achievements but fails to mention the groom at all!

It is understandable that Ida was not at Billy's wedding, but her absence from Connie's is more puzzling. Surely the '*small, informal reception*' which is referred to in the news report would have included the bride's sister, and would the competitive Connie not have wanted Ida there to see her married? On the other hand, the wedding took place on a Wednesday in university term time. Was Ida not able to take the time off? And is it possible that Connie, disabled as she was, was happy not to have her beautiful, able-bodied sister there on her wedding day?

These questions did lead me to wonder how Ida was feeling about her own personal life. She was now thirty-one, busy and active, with friends and colleagues, causes to fight for, a satisfying job and hopes for a career ahead, but did she expect to remain single? Ida's mother had once told her that she would support her career choice in every way, but that if she pursued science, she would be a social oddity, a bluestocking, and could never expect to marry or have children. But she was good-looking, charming, and she spent her working life surrounded by men; one might expect her to have had suitors. Was she actually too impressive for anyone but the most confident man? The pattern of her professional and personal life looks a very familiar one for women now: the early years spent establishing a career, then marriage in mid-thirties, followed by children before it is too late. It is impossible to know whether that was Ida's plan, or how much – if at all – she was unsettled by the flurry of marriages of her siblings.

The year 1909 ended with one further piece of family news. A card announces the birth of Mary Elizabeth Smedley on 19th December. This was the first of the four children Olive would give birth to before Billy ('*attractive but unreliable*', as Barbara comments) left her. Ida, we see from her letters, was fond of '*poor little Olive*', as she often referred to her, and did her best to support her when she was left to manage alone.

When this baby, Mary Elizabeth (always known in the family, for some reason, as 'Peter'), went on to study at St Hilda's College, Oxford, it was Ida who paid the fees and supported her through her student years. Mary Smedley went on to become the head of a girls' school in Sussex.

CHAPTER FOUR

HOME NOW UNDER SUCH SATISFACTORY FINANCIAL CONDITIONS

1910–1913

'4th February 1910
You have won scholarship.
Announcement posted.
Congratulations. Mother.'

THIS IS THE TELEGRAM THAT INFORMED IDA THAT she had been awarded the extraordinarily prestigious Beit Memorial Research Fellowship, which would determine the course of her future life. It finally established her as a recognised academic and gave her a position at the Lister Institute of Preventive Medicine in London, where she would work for the rest of her career. She was the first woman to be awarded one of these fellowships, and she kept the sheaf of congratulatory letters that followed it. One came immediately from her father:

'My Dear Ida,

    I am delighted and congratulate you most sincerely. It is delightful to think that you can come home now under such satisfactory financial conditions. I hope to see you tomorrow.

    Your affectionate Father.'

His sense that Ida's time in Manchester had been a kind of exile is palpable – as is the relief that she might be financially independent at last!

There were separate congratulations from Billy and Olive; from a cousin, who described her father missing his train home because he was going all over Birmingham trying to buy a London paper with the announcement of the award in it; and a long and generous letter from Connie, who echoed her father's pleasure at the financial reward. She also echoed the feelings of several of the women who sent their congratulations – the sense that Ida had won this not just for herself but for women more widely:

'Dearest Di,

    We are so immensely pleased at the news of your success, and especially I am delighted because it must be such a relief to feel you know exactly what you have and can plan holidays abroad and do pretty well whatever you want to do. The prospect does look rosy!

    It is also very jolly to feel work tells & makes its way in the end, even if a woman does it, and every success goes to break down the idea that women aren't to be allowed a "fair field".'

The leading suffragist Millicent Garret Fawcett congratulated her in comparable terms:

'My Dear Miss Smedley,

May I offer my very hearty congratulations on your appointment to the Beit fellowship. It gives me very sincere satisfaction and will be an advantage to the W.S. [Women's Suffrage] cause.

Believe me yours very sincerely,

M.G. Fawcett'

Nothing would have given Ida more pleasure, I think, than to feel that her success, rather than elevating her above other women, paved the way for them to achieve too. Her fame went beyond the UK. In Australia, *The Western Mail* singled her out for special mention in an article, 'Women as Inventors', including her in a group which contained Marie Curie, Hertha Ayrton (mathematician and engineer) and Marie Stopes, such was the kudos that the fellowship conferred.

Her father's reference to coming 'home' now referred to the very grand house in Russell Square to which he and Anne had recently moved. Here Ida moved in, not as the spinster daughter living under sufferance and expected to help with the running of the home, but on a basis of equality and respect. Ida was free to invite friends or colleagues home to dinner at a moment's notice, to invite friends for weekend house parties, and open the drawing rooms for BFUW and suffrage meetings.

Her scrapbooks and diaries for 1910 and 1911 show that her return to London launched her not only into a new line of research but into a whirl of social, cultural, sporting, academic and campaigning activities. She was continuing to drive the activities of the BFUW and now took on the Lyceum clubs – Connie's project, which she seems to have tired of and abandoned, leaving Ida and her mother to take on the responsibility, which was considerable; she recorded thirty-two meetings related to Lyceum business in the course of 1911 alone. And that year she spoke at nine women's suffrage meetings and chaired eleven meetings of the BFUW.

The suffrage question was by now a critical political issue, with the militant wing of the suffrage movement, the Women's Social and Political Union, encouraging and orchestrating violent protests. Hunger strikes and force-feeding in prisons were hot topics in the press, and the Liberal government at last offered a concession: they would introduce a Conciliation Bill, granting the right to vote to a small number of women who met a stringent property qualification. The WSPU agreed to suspend its campaigning activities while the bill was going through parliament, but the bill became mired in party conflict in the Commons and was dropped. Infuriated, the WSPU moved to more extreme action. Ida remained outside this. She attended, hosted and spoke at suffrage meetings, and joined marches and demonstrations, but this was tame business in the context of smashed windows, bombed buildings and postboxes on fire. Ida's memorabilia show how much she was thinking about the issue, and they include, among much else, the words and music for Ethel Smyth's rousing suffragist anthem, 'The March of the Women'; the programmes for the Great Suffrage Demonstration in Hyde Park to mark Emmeline Pankhurst's birthday; and a huge meeting at the Albert Hall, where a fundraising drive was launched with the aim of raising the vast sum of £40,000. But there was too much in her life for her to martyr herself in the suffrage cause. She was at the most exciting stage of her scientific career and was not prepared to jeopardise that – and she was enjoying a life rich with friendships, interests and pleasures.

Always on the alert for a possible romantic interest in her life (she was now thirty-three), I noticed in September 1910 the appearance of a Mr Pope. Ida attended a scientific conference in Sheffield, and though she clearly did hear some research papers, her account of the week there is mainly of excursions to places of local interest, theatre trips, dinners and receptions. She spent her time with a group of colleagues from London and Manchester, among whom Mr Pope figured. When the others left at the end of the week, she and Mr Pope went off for a walk together, and on the following day:

'I travelled up to Town with Mr Pope & Barlow, dined with Mr Pope at Frascati's and went to the Japanese Exhibition and a Queen's Hall concert.'

By most definitions, dinner, an exhibition and a concert would qualify as a date. The next day, she travelled down to Cornwall for a holiday in Helston with a different group of friends from those she was with in Sheffield – her old schoolfriend, Winifred Cullis, and her brothers – but a few days later Mr Pope arrived there too. There is nothing in her diary about her feelings for him, but over the next week she and he enjoyed solo walks to Kynance, to Pentreath and to Mullion, before she saw him off on a bus back to London. And then he disappears from the diary.

This disappearance may have been connected with the appearance at the Lister of a new fellow researcher, Hugh MacLean. He was two years younger than Ida, had taken a medical degree at Aberdeen University but was now pursuing an academic career. He had an MSc from Liverpool University and had been appointed a Senior Assistant at the Lister while working for a DSc. In his obituary in Munk's Roll, his son, Kenneth (also a doctor), describes him as follows:

'Tall in stature, he had an imposing presence. Nevertheless, beneath a self-confident exterior he was a shy man...

*He had great charm and was a good mixer, but he did
not make friends easily among his medical colleagues...
Although he retained but little of his Scottish accent, he
was a true Highlander, and his early upbringing among
the Inverness-shire hills coloured his whole life.'*[8]

His early upbringing had imbued him, among other things,
with a passion for golf, and it seems more than coincidental
that early in 1911, Ida's diary starts to record games of golf. She
played regularly through that year, recording for the first time
on 27th October, *'golf with Dr MacLean'*. Was this her intention
all along? This is not actually her first mention of him in her
diary: four days earlier she had invited him to a Lyceum Club
'Celtic Languages' dinner, along with John Ledingham – another
Scottish colleague (later Sir John Ledingham and director of
the Lister) – and Winifred Cullis. Did the Celtic Languages
topic give her an opportunity to make an approach to the shy
Scot in the lab, an approach given perfect respectability by
the inclusion in the party of another colleague and another
professional woman? Did she actually choose the topic for the
dinner with Hugh MacLean in mind – and did the golf have
the same purpose? If she was pursuing him, she succeeded, and
they saw each other regularly from that time – mainly for golf,
occasionally for dinner at Ida's home.

She was, of course, also working. She published a research
paper in the *Journal of the Chemical Society* in 1911, less
than a year after she had started work at the Lister. She was
now researching the synthesis of fatty acids – the work with
significant implications for diet and health which she would
continue for the rest of her career, and in which she would
become the recognised expert.[9] The paper, entitled 'The

8   Munk's Roll *Lives of the Physicians* (Royal College of Physicians) p257.
9   See Appendix I for a summary of this work, written by her collaborator,
     L.C.A. Nunn, for the obituary in *Nature* vol 154, 22nd July 1944.

Condensation of Crotonaldehyde',[10] was followed by a paper in the *Biochemical Journal* on 'The Fatty Acids of Butter'.[11] She had made the move into the newly recognised field of biochemistry, and she had begun to establish her reputation there. Research papers published in the professional journals were then, and still are, the currency of academic scientific research. They are the means of communicating findings, but they are also the means of establishing a professional profile. The number of publications, the status of the journal in which they appear and the number of times they are cited by others working in the field all go to make a reputation among one's peers. Ida's record of published papers put her in a commanding position.

Building her own achievements and actively supporting the cause of women's suffrage, she was also pursuing her own route to improving women's opportunities through the BFUW. The organisation was busy making links with girls' schools and encouraging girls to go on to university, was promoting better career opportunities for women doctors, and was offering funding for women students to go on to postgraduate research. She was adept at getting publicity for the BFUW's activities: she was attractive and eloquent, and the newspapers liked her.

Towards the end of 1912, the first annual dinner for Beit fellows in medical research was held at the fashionable Trocadero restaurant in London; Ida kept her dinner card, which had been signed by ten current fellows, including three more women, two elected in 1911 and one in 1912. Ida's appointment, it seems, had started a trend. This is reinforced by a cutting from *The Times* reporting on further

10 *Journal of the Chemical Society CLXXXV* 'The Condensation of Croton-aldehyde' by Ida Smedley (Beit Memorial Research Fellow).

11 *Biochemical Journal* 'The Fatty Acids of Butter' by Ida Smedley (Beit Memorial Research Fellow) January 01 1912.

elections to Beit fellowships. It notes that Ida Smedley was elected in 1910, reappointed in 1911 and 1912, and had now had her appointment extended for a further year 'by *special recommendation of the advisory panel*'. It goes on to report the election of two further women to fellowships: Elsie Dalziel (trained in Sydney) to work at the Lister Institute on gastroenteric disease in infants, and Helen Pixel (mentioned earlier in Ida's diary as a golf partner) to work on parasitic protozoa at Bedford College and the Lister. For Ida, who took such pleasure in other women's achievements, these awards must have been a delight – through winning the award and using it to do excellent work she had not put herself apart from other women as too exceptional to be emulated, but had opened a door for them by her example. And she must have been pleased to find herself with some female colleagues in the workplace. When she joined the Lister, there were only two other women there: microbiologist Harriette Chick and Janet Lane-Claypon, a founder of epidemiology. By 1933, forty per cent of the Lister's staff were women.

At the same time, Ida's courtship with Hugh MacLean was flourishing (although he remained '*Dr MacLean*' in her diary for some time). Through 1912, they continued to play golf, and I enjoyed a diary entry on 7th April:

'*At lab 10–3 Dr MacLean dined here and we examined Lotte with the stethoscope to see if we could diagnose the number of her forthcoming pups. Owing to her restlessness not very successful.*'

Although he is still '*Dr MacLean*', there is definitely a ring of frivolity about the evening; I liked the image of this serious pair bent over the pregnant dog, listening for heartbeats. In September, she went for a nine-day walking holiday in

Cornwall with her friend Beatrice Thomas, and recorded, on 30th September, the day of her return: *'Hugh and Beatrice dined here.'* He was invited round for an immediate reunion, and this is the first entry in which he is referred to as *'Hugh'*.

For Ida, 1913 was a triumphant year. She started it with her Beit Fellowship extended and her work at the Lister secure. Then she and Hugh MacLean had a paper published in the *Journal of Physiology*, 'The Utilisation of Different Sugars by the Normal Heart', and in February, she was elected as one of the first three women members of the newly formed Biochemical Society. In March, she and Hugh married, and in April, she was awarded a $1,000 research award. In July, she had another paper published in the *Biochemical Journal*, and all this was recognised in an article about her which appeared in the fashionable journal *The Queen, the Ladies' Newspaper*, later that month.

Election to the Biochemical Society must have been a particularly sweet success, given that the Chemical Society was still barring its doors to women, despite the best efforts of Ida, Martha Whiteley and the BFUW. The new society (set up as the Biochemical Club) had initially excluded women when an amendment to the proposed constitution was passed, at its inaugural meeting in July 1911, by seventeen votes to nine. A year later, however, the decision was reversed by twenty-four votes to seven and three women members were admitted in February 1913: Ida, Harriette Chick and Muriel Wheldale, a fellow alumna of Ida's from King Edward VI and Newnham, a pioneering plant biochemist and lecturer at Cambridge. Fifteen years later, Ida would become the first woman to be elected chairman of the society.

Following close on her election came the marriage; the memorabilia contain an *'AT HOME'* invitation for Thursday 27th March at 9.00 pm from Mr and Mrs Smedley *'on the eve*

of the marriage of their daughter Ida with Dr Hugh MacLean'
and a printed card with 'Ida Smedley' in the top left corner,
followed by 'with Mr & Mrs Hugh MacLean's compliments,
March 28 1913, 58 Overstrand Mansions, Battersea Park SW'.

The At Home invitation gives the Smedley's address as 2
Carlyle Mansions, Cheyne Walk, Chelsea – their new home,
to which they had moved very recently. Both in their sixties,
they may have felt that Ida's marriage freed them to give up
the grand house in Russell Square, which would no longer be
needed to entertain Ida's friends or host suffrage and BFUW
meetings, but although they were downsizing, they were not
moving downmarket. Cheyne Walk, Chelsea was a highly
desirable address and Carlyle Mansions, named after the
writer Thomas Carlyle, was home, over the years, to so many
well-known writers – Henry James, Erskine Childers, T.S.
Eliot, Somerset Maugham, Ian Fleming – that, inevitably,
London's literati came to call it Writers' Block. Overstrand
Mansions, in Prince of Wales Drive, where Ida and Hugh set
up home, was across the river in Battersea – a cheaper area,
though they overlooked the park and were close to the river.

The wedding, it seems, was a small affair, like those of Billy
and Connie. None of them had church weddings and there is
no mention of church-going in Ida's diaries. Barbara MacLean
has a story to tell about her grandfather which sheds some
light on this. William Smedley grew up in a Baptist household
and was a committed member of the congregation as a young
man, but he was persuaded by an elderly 'pillar' of the church
to underwrite a bill for a large sum of money (Barbara believes
it was £3,000, but is not sure; if so, that would be more than
£300,000 today). The elderly pillar absconded, and William
Smedley was left to pay the debt. He paid it off during the years
when his children were young and felt that they were deprived
as a result. He left the church and did not join another.

Hugh MacLean had grown up in a Presbyterian family, and Ida did consider a church wedding. According to Barbara, she wrote to a cousin of hers, Canon Lonsdale Ragg, to ask if he would marry them in her parish church. Canon Ragg approached the vicar at Chelsea Old Church, who responded that he did not consider that his church was a suitable venue for what appeared to be a wedding between an atheist and a Presbyterian. They were married at Chelsea Register Office and went on to honeymoon in Fowey. Ida kept a postcard of Fowey Golf Club. Golf would feature largely in their married life. Barbara writes that golf was her father's passion and that her mother was never a very good golfer, only once reducing her handicap below the 36 maximum. It is rather appealing to find this multi-talented woman persevering with something at which she did not excel.

She returned from the honeymoon to the news that she had been awarded the Ellen Richards prize of $1,000, awarded for *the most important contribution to Science* in the previous year, and then followed the article in *The Queen*:

The article is remarkably accurate in its account of her career. It also begins the thirty-year ambivalence that was to follow about how this anomalous figure – a married woman with a DSc who had retained her maiden name alongside her married name – was to be addressed or referred to. In the letters written to her, the articles written about her and the official invitations issued to her, she is variously 'Dr Smedley-MacLean', 'Mrs Smedley-MacLean', 'Mrs I.S. MacLean', 'Mrs MacLean', 'Mrs Hugh MacLean', 'Dr Ida MacLean' and 'Dr MacLean'. She herself made a distinction between her work life and its associated activities, in which she was Dr Smedley-MacLean, and her family life, in which she was happy to be Mrs MacLean, but others – even her feminist friends – were more confused. She, by contrast, always referred in her diaries to colleagues with doctorates, male or female, as 'Dr'.

DR IDA SMEDLEY MACLEAN.
A Distinguished Scientific Investigator.

WE referred last week to the fact that Mrs MacLean had been awarded the Ellen Richards prize of 1000 dollars by the American Association for the Advancement of Research by Women for her work on *The Biochemical Synthesis of Fatty Acids*. Mrs MacLean, formerly Miss Ida Smedley, was educated at King Edward's High School, Birmingham, and Newnham College, Cambridge. She afterwards studied chemistry with Professor

[Neame.

MRS IDA SMEDLEY MACLEAN, D.Sc.

Armstrong at the Central Technical College, and obtained the degree of Doctor of Science at the University of London. She was appointed in 1906 assistant lecturer in chemistry at the Victoria University, Manchester, and resigned that post in 1910 on being elected one of the first ten Beit Memorial Medical Research Fellows. During the last three years Mrs MacLean has been working at the Lister Institute of Preventive Medicine, where her researches on the biochemical synthesis of fats have been carried out.

The photograph that accompanies the article is one of the best pictures of her to be found. Obviously a professional studio shot, it shows the woman I expected: attractive and confident, with a clear-eyed gaze, an alert tilt of the head, and a determined set to her mouth – a woman very definitely in her prime.

CHAPTER FIVE

PROBLEMS OF NATIONAL IMPORTANCE

1914–1918

In 1983, Professor A.C. Chibnall, the longest-serving secretary of the Biochemical Society, was interviewed about his memories of the society's early days. Prompted to recall Dr Ida Smedley-MacLean, he replied, '*Mrs MacLean. Yes, she was at Manchester. She worked for a time as Robinson's assistant. And then she married MacLean.*'

There is so much wrong with this assessment of Ida's career that it is difficult to know where to begin: the name, for a start, of course – '*Mrs MacLean*' – in the context of her academic career; the mention only of Manchester, ignoring her years of prestigious work at the Lister Institute; the failure to mention her chairmanship of the Biochemical Society. What is most striking, though, is the way he defines her in terms of her relationship with two men – and he is wrong in both cases. Ida was not Robert Robinson's assistant; they were colleagues, both teaching and researching at Manchester (Robert Robinson's wife, Gertrude Walsh Robinson, was his research collaborator) and marrying Hugh MacLean was not, as Chibnall seems to imply, the end of Ida Smedley's independent career.

No doubt Ida anticipated that the pattern of her life and of her work would be changed by marriage. For a start, she was no longer free of household concerns with the benefits of her parents' large domestic staff. She had a home of her own to run and no experience of doing such a thing. It is clear that she had no intention of giving up work when she married, though she was in uncharted waters and there were setbacks. It was still legal at that time for employers to dismiss a woman if she married, and although Ida was supported by her own funding (now from the Ellen Richards Prize), the Lister could still have denied her lab space. And then she was pregnant. In the spring of 1914, she was invited to apply for a professorship in biochemistry at London University, but she told Barbara that the selection committee, nervous anyway about the appointment of a woman, wrote off her application when she told them that she was pregnant. The committee's decision made no sense in practical terms: Ida, like every other middle-class mother at the time, would be employing a nanny to look after the baby. Her being pregnant, however, served to place her, in the committee's minds, on the other side of an invisible barrier, excluding her from the world of serious work, committing her to the domestic.

In the event, the demands of war cancelled out the drawbacks of motherhood. Ida's son, Kenneth, was born in November 1914, three months after the outbreak of war, and she offered her services for war work. Her old friend and colleague from her Manchester days, Chaim Weizmann, had approached the War Office with a proposal for producing acetone through fermentation. The production of acetone was essential for making explosives, since German blockades were preventing the importing of cordite for this purpose. The

War Office authorised the work but offered little in the way of practical support. Ida offered her lab at the Lister for the initial experimental work. An institute for preventive medicine was an improbable place for this kind of work, but these were war conditions, and continuing to work there, though under the auspices of the Admiralty, meant that she was only a short walk from her home in Battersea, able to go home at lunch time to see (and feed?) the baby.

This is a good place to bring in an excellent dissertation[12] by Cambridge MA student Will Peck. He writes about Ida as a paradigm of the way women scientists' war work was undervalued during World War I. Describing Ida's work, he writes:

> 'The work was primarily biochemical, concerning the expansion of the production of acetone by fermentation to an industrial scale. Acetone is a crucial ingredient in the production of cordite; it serves as the solvent which allows the extrusion of the filaments of explosives. Because of this the scaling up of the production of acetone was extremely important to the British Admiralty, given the cessation of acetone imports following the outbreak of conflict. Smedley-MacLean's precise role within the project is poorly documented… but it is reasonable to assume that she was likely a significant contributor to the project's ultimate success, based on her later work and extensive publications.'

He argues for the significance of her contribution on the basis of her successful later work; I would suggest that she had already proved herself. She was nearly forty when she started

---

12 Peck, W. *Ida Smedley Maclean: Cambridge, Women and Science in the First World War*, (unpublished MA dissertation).

on this project and had been working as a research scientist for nearly twenty years. By 1917, pregnant with Barbara, she was running the operation in the absence of Weizmann, who had been sent on a government mission to Palestine, so by then she was regarded as his second-in-command. What is disappointing is that Weizmann himself makes no mention of Ida's contribution in his own memoir.[13] His account of his wartime research team goes as follows:

> 'A group of chemists had to be trained in the process. I took over the laboratory of the Lister Institute in Chelsea and there I began to train a number of young people in this branch of chemistry. From Chelsea, I sent them out to the various distilleries [gin distilleries which were taken over for the purpose]. The young English scientists were excellent men to work with.'

Why does he fail to mention that one of these 'young people' or 'excellent men' was an experienced woman only three years younger than himself, with vital biochemical expertise? Is it because this would detract from the image of this squad of dynamic young men being dispatched to their posts around the country in military style? Or is it simply that to mention the anomalous Ida would interrupt the sweep of his narrative? He makes the same kind of omission when he writes about settling in at Manchester University when he and his wife first arrived in England:

> 'I feel I cannot stress too much the kindness which my wife and I encountered from my colleagues at the University. They were a remarkable group of men.'

---

13 Weizmann, C. *Trial and Error* (1949).

And he goes on to say how kind *the wives of colleagues'* were to his wife, Vera. There is no mention at all of Ida, yet it is clear from her diaries and letters that she befriended Vera and that she maintained a friendship with both of them over many, many years: there are mentions of dinners, theatre visits, weekends spent with Ida in London, Christmas 1909 spent with her family, time spent in Switzerland together and happy reunions in later years, quite apart from the special closeness that developed during the war. Her absence from his memoir lowers him in my estimation, yet it can hardly have been deliberate or malicious; Weizmann was not against women having professional careers – he took his wife's career as a doctor very seriously. It is more, it seems, an illustration of how women have been written out of narratives simply because they are anomalous. To give them special mention among the generalities would be to give them prominence; to brush them aside in the general sweep of the narrative too often seems the easier option.

Whatever Weizmann omitted to say, there is no doubt that Ida was deeply involved in the research, and indeed in the struggles Weizmann had with the War Office in running the project. There are only a few genuine diary entries among Ida's wartime records: they mainly take the form of press cuttings about the war, intermingled with photographs of the children and the occasional theatre programme. There are, however, diary entries for January 1916, when she went to the Admiralty's chemical warfare factory at Holton Heath in Dorset for the crucial trial in the acetone project before it went into production. Typically, Ida made an enjoyable outing of this work trip, staying at a hotel in Bournemouth with baby Kenneth and his nanny, and introducing him to the seaside. Her diary's juxtaposition of maternal doting and professional preoccupations will be familiar to anyone who has combined work and babies:

'Jan 1ˢᵗ 1916

Kenneth & Nannie & I have arrived at Weston Hall Hotel, Bournemouth. Kenneth was a very good boy, made friends with everyone in the railway carriage. He has 10 teeth now, can walk by himself for short distances, across the nursery & down the passage & says quite a lot of things. Then he makes sounds like all the animals & knows quite a good deal of what is said to him. His hat is his ta -ta & his shoes, shu-shu. He is very affectionate especially to his Nannie & to me; and altogether is a most friendly attractive little baby & very imitative... The big experiment at Poole starts tomorrow, the final trial for making acetone before the big plant is built. Dr W is very excited but Gavronsky & Thaysen who have just arrived are very calm as they are quite confident that everything is well. 9.30 p.m. I shall now feed Kenneth & go to bed.'

Kenneth Smedley MacLean

Will Peck makes the bold assertion that Ida's work gives her a claim to an unrecognised influence on the attitude of the British government to the founding of the State of Israel; according to Weizmann's obituary in *The New York Times*, Weizmann was summoned by Lloyd George after the end of the war to be thanked for his service to the country and asked how he could be rewarded. Weizmann replied that he wanted '*a national home for my people*'.[14] This, it can be argued, led ultimately to the Balfour Declaration, the establishment of the state of Israel and Weizmann's election as its first president in 1948. Ida was strongly supportive of the campaign for a Jewish homeland, and she was an unselfish woman, so perhaps we can assume that she may have been happy for Weizmann to claim the credit that earnt him government support.

There is, actually, a question to be answered about how Ida felt about her war work. Her diary entries at the time show that she was fully committed, and she was delighted with the success of the Poole experiment, seeing the acetone rushing off as they had hoped; but Barbara, in her memoir, gives a startlingly different account of her mother's war work: '*While at the Lister Institute, she also acted as a consultant to the Admiralty and the Gas Warfare Board, but was rarely called on for advice*'. This must have been Ida's own account – or Barbara's understanding of it – but it seems deliberately to underplay her active part. It can hardly be the case that she would have been regarded as an expert to be '*called on for advice*' if she had still been working on fat metabolism, nor would she have been left in charge of the laboratory. Three official letters of thanks, sent to her at the end of the war (one from Winston Churchill as Minister for Munitions) leave no doubt that she had been involved in serious war work.

---

14 'Chaim Weizmann of Israel is Dead' *The New York Times* November 9, 1952.

So, she chose to understate her work, or Barbara later understated it for reasons of her own. Barbara was born in 1917, so it would probably have been nearly ten years after the end of the war that she asked her mother about her war work, and by that time a certain revulsion had set in generally about the terrible carnage of the war. Perhaps by that time, Ida was not keen to tell her daughter that she had worked on more efficient methods of blowing men up.

There is an intriguing reflection on the issue of Ida's war work in a recent play by community playwright Frank Hatt about Connie. Entitled *The Amazing and Preposterous Constance Smedley* and based on a store of letters and press cuttings unearthed at Connie's former home, the play tells the story of Connie's life and struggle with disability, and has a major role for Ida. Hatt portrays Ida, for the most part, as a stiff, unimaginative scientist, contrasting with her creative, emotional sister (a characterisation of Ida quite at odds with the lively, humorous, affectionate woman who emerges from her diaries), but he writes one scene in which he imagines Ida's conflict over working for the Admiralty, and he gives her a speech in which she sums up her sense of having no choice:

> 'There is an understanding that if you have a family you can't go on with your career. But this is not exactly a rule. They have some discretion. I've been given to understand that if I'm a good girl and go and do my bit for the war effort, then a blind eye will be turned to my lapse into fertility. If not, then I must take the consequences.'

The speech is the work of the playwright's imagination, of course, and the tone does not match that of the Ida we meet in the diaries, but though she had a lab at the Lister, she was not yet on the permanent staff and her position was quite insecure; it may have been difficult to resist the war work, if she had wanted to. And there is an indication that she was rewarded by the government: from the end of the war her research was funded by the Department of Scientific and Industrial Research.

These war years held their terrors, but in war, as in so much else, Ida was fortunate. Both her brother and her husband served in the war but, unlike millions of wives, sisters and mothers, she did not have her life blighted by loss. Hugh was commissioned in the Royal Army Medical Corps with the rank of captain. He had developed an interest in renal pathology in the previous two years, and in 1917 was sent to France to investigate the large number of cases of nephritis among the British troops there. He set up a laboratory behind the lines in Etaples, which was severely damaged by bombing in early 1918, but he was unhurt. Billy fought in the Artists' Rifles throughout the war, and was wounded in Palestine, but suffered no long-term damage. Connie and Maxwell, both pacifists, avoided the war by moving to the USA in 1915, remaining there for the next seven years. In another of her loose diary pages, however, Ida did record a family death, writing that Alick MacLean died on the Somme in July 1916:

'*August 14th. A month ago on July 14th, we heard that Alick had been killed at the Somme... he was doing sentry duty & he wouldn't wake the man who should have been on duty, a piece of shell struck him & he was killed instantaneously. Hugh has had a letter from his friend. Alick is buried near Fricourt.*'

Ida did not know enough at this point to be sceptical about the standard assurance that Alick was '*killed instantaneously*'.

There is less information about the MacLean family

than about the Smedleys, but Hugh was the eldest of several brothers and I assume that Alick was one of those brothers. Hugh's father was a tenant farmer in Aberarder near Inverness, and Ida and Hugh made a miserable journey to see his family and share their mourning. Hugh had made a trip up to Inverness earlier in the year – perhaps to see his brother before he went to the front.

In the scrapbooks for these years, the personal dramas of the diary pages jostle with assiduously gathered newspaper cuttings about the war, baby photographs, and the usual theatre and concert programmes, invitations and menus. There is an intriguing item among the menus: a luncheon given, on 6th December 1916, by the Artists' Rifles for the ladies of the Lyceum Club. Since brother Billy was serving with the Artists' Rifles, this was probably his work. There is also a programme for an entertainment at the same event – held at Hare Hall Camp, Romford. Billy was not among the performers, but the programme includes piano and violin solos, songs, recitations and magic. The Lyceum Club reciprocated with an Artists' Rifles dinner, at which one of the hostesses was *'Mrs Smedley MacLean DSc'.* The contrast between the grief in Aberarder and this Home Counties wartime entertainment feels rather stark.

The armistice brought a reward for the women who had worked for the war effort – a reward which seemed to vindicate the suffrage movement's contentious decision at the outset to support the war. Emmeline and Christabel Pankhurst had declared an immediate end to disruptive action from the WSPU, but other groups within the suffrage movement were committed to taking a pacifist line and distancing themselves from a conflict generated by male aggression, and when a vote of the National Union of Women's Suffrage Societies went in favour of supporting the war, there was a flood of resignations.

The work that women did during the conflict – dirty, dangerous, exhausting and ill-paid – won them (partially) their battle for the vote. One of the arguments that were put forward against allowing women to vote was that they would be concerned only with domestic policy and would not be strong on defence issues (aka keen on war). In 1917, Prime Minister Lloyd George told the House of Commons:

> 'I myself, as I believe many others, no longer regard the woman suffrage question from the standpoint we occupied before the war... the Women's Cause in England now presents an unanswerable case.'

A leader in the *Daily Mail* offered the opinion that:

> 'The old argument against giving women the franchise was that they were useless in war. But we have found that we could not carry on the war without them.'

Ida kept a programme for a Women Workers' Demonstration, held at Queen's Hall, London on February 20th, 1917 and organised by the NUWSS. The suffragists knew that popular opinion was turning in their favour and they mustered all their forces to press home their advantage. The programme lists the seventeen suffrage societies which took part and the representatives from trades, professions and organisations who formed the platform party. There are seventy-five of them: workers in traditional women's fields mixed with those in the new jobs opened to them by the exigencies of war. They are listed alphabetically, from actresses, artists, ambulance drivers and accountants; through bus drivers, chainmakers, dentists and electrical power workers; lamplighters, munitions workers and oxyacetalene welders;

policewomen, railway women and scientific research workers to van drivers and weavers.

The Representation of the People Act of 1918 gave the right to vote to women over thirty who met a property qualification. It was to be ten years before the Equality of Representation Act gave women voting rights on a par with men's, but the case had been made and the argument had been won. Perhaps as a result of this concession to women's rights, another law was passed which ended Ida's ten-year battle for membership of the Chemical Society. In 1919, the Sex Disqualification Act was removed from the statute book; discrimination on the grounds of gender or marital status was no longer legitimised. Though many organisations found ways of circumventing this, the Chemical Society finally gave in, and there was a unanimous vote to admit women members. In 1920, twenty-one women were elected as fellows, including Ida and Martha Whiteley. Ida established a dining club for women members, meeting at the London Lyceum club. This was a pattern she adopted early and continued throughout her career – the double strategy of pushing at the doors of male exclusiveness while, at the same time, setting up parallel women's networks. She might be criticised for demanding both access to male bastions and the right to female exclusiveness, but given how heavily the cards were stacked against professional women, I feel inclined to forgive her.

CHAPTER SIX

WOMEN WITH BRAINS FOR OUR AMBASSADORS: BFUW AND IFUW

1919–1929

FOR SEVERAL YEARS AFTER THE WAR, IDA KEPT HER records in hardback A4 size albums, which burst with evidence of her own vigorous life and the lives of her husband, children, siblings and parents. One of the most striking is the album for 1920. She started the year with a two-month speaking tour of the United States – a courageous and, as it turned out, exhausting enterprise. She was leaving two small children behind: Kenneth, aged six, and Barbara only just two. Kenneth, in his brief account of his childhood that Barbara included in her family memoir, writes of his mother:

> 'Throughout my early childhood she was working at the Lister Institute just north of Chelsea Bridge so that although I saw a great deal of her and we became very close, I was mainly cared for by a nanny until I went to prep school.'

Ida was a devoted mother; her diaries are alive with the pleasure and pride she took in her children, and are packed with photographs, programmes for school plays and prize-givings, infant artwork, pieces of juvenilia (even someone's first writing copybook), accounts of outings and holidays with the children and concerns about their health and progress. However, she was not only a working mother but a public figure in her work for the BFUW, and she could have done none of that without a nanny and other staff at home. But this was usual for a prosperous middle-class family, even for one where the wife did nothing more with her time than take drives and pay visits. Of course, Ida must have missed her husband and children during her three months away, and worried about them (though her ability not to worry pointlessly does emerge as one of the secrets of her success).

She travelled alone around the USA, but she travelled out with Caroline Spurgeon, Professor of English Literature at Bedford College, London, and the first woman in England to be made a professor. Winifred Cullis was with them for part of the time, too. She had distinguished herself during the war, working on the health of the men being sent into battle, and she had been awarded an OBE, as well as being appointed Professor of Physiology at London University. Neither she nor Caroline Spurgeon married or had children, and they both achieved professorships. Ida, pregnant when her chance came, had not, but on this occasion, it was Ida who was the main attraction; the large bundle of press cuttings from US papers, including several from *The New York Times* and *The Washington Post*, lead with the visit from this 'Distinguished English Woman Scientist'. The publicity around her visit was as nothing compared with the razzmatazz surrounding the tour of the USA that Marie Curie made two years later to raise funds for her research. She was showered with honorary doctorates and awards, and huge crowds turned out to see her. Ida was the better public speaker, though, and while Curie had her three adult daughters with her on her tour, Ida did hers alone.

Ida's visit was on behalf of the BFUW and at the invitation of the American Federation of University Women. One of the aims was to bolster support for an International Federation of University Women which had been initiated the previous year; the other, related aim, was for Ida to learn more about the American model of fundraising and philanthropic giving, which was far more strongly established than anything in the UK. While Professors Spurgeon and Cullis made only brief appearances confined to New York, Ida undertook a ferociously demanding solo speaking tour from coast to coast of the USA.

Starting with five hectic days in New York, where she was besieged by news reporters, she travelled by train across the country to St Louis and then, via Kansas City and with a stop to view the Grand Canyon, to California ('*I am tired of 4 nights in the train & long for better toilet arrangements*'). There she spent eight days and went to Los Angeles, Palo Alto and San Francisco before continuing her journey to Portland, Oregon, to Seattle and to Washington State. Then followed a forty-eight-hour train journey from Spokane in Washington State to Minneapolis, and on to Milwaukee, Wisconsin, before returning to New York via Buffalo and the Niagara Falls. At each stage, she had a packed programme of speaking engagements – bespoke talks on subjects ranging from 'Fat Metabolism and Vitamins' to 'The Effect of War on Educational Methods' and 'The Influence of Women on International Relations' – as well as visits to hospitals, laboratories, baby clinics, schools, colleges and universities, art galleries, museums, and power stations. In between, she ate a relentless series of lunches, teas and dinners, each with a fresh collection of invited guests, eager to seek her opinion not only on women's education, but on President Hoover, labour relations in the UK and the politics of the Middle East. Impressively, she was able to note the names of her fellow guests on each occasion. Did she carry a notebook with her? Or was there a practice of exchanging cards? If there was, she did not keep them among her mementoes of the trip.

The outgoing sea voyage was taxing enough. She left England on 14th January for a winter crossing of the Atlantic, and her diary of the trip opens with the following lines:

> 'The voyage.
> And now another day is done,
> And when we see tomorrow's sun
> Another day will be begun.
> Let's hope that too will soon be done.'

It is an uncharacteristically downbeat sentiment, but quite a mild response to a week of being seasick.

> 'For a week we had rough seas & a swell officially described as from moderate to heavy – two days after leaving a "moderate gale". Anyway, it was bad & I spent a very uncomfortable week chiefly in the cabin. Today is intensely cold, exhilarating tho' I have to retire into the library at intervals to thaw my feet.'

They docked first in Halifax, Nova Scotia, and there was an incident there that troubled her enough for her to put it in her diary:

> 'We watched the immigrants disembark, one woman with

three children nearly returned to Liverpool because they were unvaccinated & only after long persuasion did she give way – consent to it being carried out on board & the pathetic little family finally left us.'

It is a characteristic response from her – both to notice and to care.

When they docked at New York, Ida and Caroline Spurgeon were met by a group from the AFUW, including Ida's hostess Alice Parsons, whom Ida liked immediately, and who became a lifelong friend. The visiting British academics were sufficiently distinguished for their luggage to be rushed through customs in record time. Alice and Edgerton Parsons and their two little daughters were charming and hospitable, but the pressures of this high-profile trip were apparent almost immediately. Having arrived at noon on Saturday 23rd January, after a ten-day voyage, she wrote of the next day:

'On Sunday we had a nice quiet morning & after lunch the unexpected happened – reporter after reporter called to interview me & Mrs Parsons delivered me over to them. There were about 10 & one man to take my photograph. When I got over my annoyance it was faintly amusing. They asked me every kind of question – "what is behind it – over here you know we think Hoover is too pro-British – are you over in connection with that?" or "What is your opinion of British foreign policy in Egypt?" There were 3 girls & 7 men. One of the girls a Scotch girl from the Tribune gave us an excellent report. She was so pleased when I said that in Scotland the feeling for education was so much stronger than in England. She said "Someone asked me yesterday if there were any schools in Scotland",

I shall certainly use that... Some of the reporters were very nice boys – one or two rather impossible specimens.'

So began a rather difficult relationship with reporters throughout her trip; publicity was important for her cause, but they besieged her when she was exhausted, asked her the wrong questions and misreported her answers. At a later stage in her diary of the trip, she gathered a collection of *'pressisms',* including:

'At St Louis – The title of my lecture "The influence of women on international relations" appeared as "The influenza of women and international relations." As an influenza epidemic was raging at the time, this was of topical interest.

At New York – The gentleman who began "Well Mrs MacLean what is behind this Federation – we think Hoover is too pro-British is it anything to do with that?"– gave me as headlines "MacLean says American education in every respect better than British." – I had refused to criticise American education on the ground that I had only been in the country 24 hours & hadn't seen a single educational institution.

At Portland – A statement I made that I had learnt more by talking to Americans about the political position here for 2 evenings than I had gathered by reading newspapers at home for years – this was transcribed as "Reading American newspapers for 2 days had taught me more than reading British newspapers for many days at home."

Another from a New York interview was that my face showed my long line "of Scottish ancestry".'

Her comment, *'Some of the reporters were very nice boys – one* or two rather impossible specimens', is characteristic of the way she often nailed the people she met with neat little fingernail sketches: 'a capable, intelligent woman but rather convinced of her own importance', 'a very nice, rather flippant woman', 'both very kind and rather deaf so that they speak at the same time'. Mostly, she responded positively to the people she met, especially the AFUW women, who were mostly young, with young children – a new generation of college-educated women.

Always ready to find interest and pleasure in new experiences, she enjoyed seeing the sights. She loved being driven round New York, magical under snow, and found the skyscrapers unexpectedly fine; she appreciated the Rockies and Niagara Falls, and she wrote an eloquent description of the 'magic, unpaintable and indescribable' Grand Canyon. She was not blind, though, to the implications of turning the canyon into a tourist attraction, and concluded:

'The hotel is wrong & we are wrong it should belong to the Indians to the trappers & hunters not to the tourists, but I am glad we have seen it.'

She was appreciative of the warm hospitality she received, she enjoyed many of the people that she met, she was hugely impressed by state-of-the-art laboratories and hospitals and by flourishing university campuses and women's colleges, but however positive she tried to be, it is clear that she became exhausted. One of the striking things about her diaries in general is that she never seemed to get tired. She recorded whirlwinds of activity but seems always to have had the energy for them. In the American diary, however, she is 'very tired', 'too tired', 'completely tired' and 'tired out', and, most uncharacteristically, at the end of her trip she cancelled some engagements. And she became disenchanted with making speeches. Initially, she was thrilled by the response from her audience:

> 'The atmosphere was friendly & my speech on the International Federation went excellently. I sat down to cries of "Brilliant" & "Splendid" & really got a first class reception.'

But ten days later, after four uncomfortable nights on a train, she arrived in Los Angeles where, unusually, she was put up in a hotel rather than in someone's home and found herself in a very noisy bedroom overlooking a tramway junction. This was a poor preparation for the next day which brought a badly handled event, where other speakers overran and her talk was rudely curtailed when 'the chairman tugged my coat tails and I sat abruptly down'. There was some compensation when, afterwards, 'Two mothers came & said they should send their daughters to study chemistry in England after they had graduated having been impressed by what I had said,' but she was disenchanted, and concluded, 'The worst of it all is that I am becoming bored stiff by speaking – am no longer nervous but very bored by it & long for the peace of home & laboratory.' This is the closest she allowed herself to an admission of homesickness.

In Oregon, infuriated by some of the right-wing views on British politics to which she had been subjected, she managed to use a lecture to mount a spirited defence of the British railwaymen's strike, called in protest against cuts in their wages, which had been put up during the war and then reduced afterwards:

> 'We dined with old Mrs Corbett & proceeded to hear Coningsly Danson lecture. Very journalistic & hostile to labour, his account of the railway strike being that they

were taking advantage of the starvation of Europe to further their own selfish ends – the strike had been broken by the returned soldiers & the girls who had worked in the war. Lord Montagu had driven the express from Bournemouth, Lady Drogheda had acted as a porter at Waterloo. The next day at the Civic League Luncheon about 300 present, I introduced this as an example of differences in British opinion – giving my reason for the strike... I was very restrained & tried to be fair but I felt labour must have something said for it. The cheapest kind of unskilled labour here gets 4 ½ dollars a day. The sympathy elicited for the railway strikers when I told them their Bolshevist demand was for a minimum wage of 15 dollars a week can be imagined.'

She began too, to voice criticism of the American attitude to wealth. Initially she was impressed by the free flow of money and the ease of fundraising in the USA:

'On Tuesday I drove down with Mrs Parsons to her office to see how the campaign for funds for Smith College was organised. They do it wonderfully beginning with their graduates then making lists of millionaires, their hobbies, their interests, any members of their families who have been to college. They say they are applying the methods which have been so successful in raising money for the Red Cross.'

And she enjoyed the spacious homes and comfortable lifestyle of her hostesses on her travels – the houses were *'beautiful'*, *'lovely'*, *'charming'*, *'delightful'* – but later, *'beautiful residences'* acquired inverted commas, and she concluded, *'I feel quite markedly here that the standard of success is the dollar & that beautiful residences & fortunes count for more here than in England.'*

On her return to New York, she was delighted to be back with the Parsons family, who gave her the warmest of welcomes and took her to hear Caruso sing. Unfortunately, she subsequently involved them in a disastrous dinner party. Connie and Max, who had gone to the USA to avoid the war, were still there. They had been to the Parsons for dinner when Ida first arrived in New York, and on that occasion things seem to have gone well enough, but a return invitation to dinner with them did not turn out happily:

'*Sunday*

We dined with Connie & Max who had a Professor & Mrs Farnsworth, a Mr & Mrs Davis & Miss Weir to meet us. The service was bad, Miss Weir, a most pretentious person, who infuriated me by her condescension to Edgerton Parsons as only a businessman who gave no reaction to the community. It would not have mattered if they had been simple but they weren't & Connie & Max thought them first rate people. I felt horribly depressed & I had to speak out to the Parsons who felt as I did that the whole atmosphere was absolutely unreal & it worried me to feel Connie & Max pay such attention to externals, such as their belief in Miss Weir's Yale degree & couldn't see that she has two exceptional people in the two Parsons. The next morning somebody rang E.P. up at breakfast to tell him not to open a letter that had been sent to him about removing his ships from a pier. He is evidently having a very worrying business time & I felt so sorry I had taken them to Connie's on Sunday.'

The unpleasantness and the embarrassment of the occasion is

conveyed vividly, as is her loyalty to the Parsons. Apart from a brief note of a lunchtime meeting the next day to discuss IFUW matters, this is the end of her account of the trip. Since the 'diary' is a collection of loose pages, mixed with newspaper cuttings, postcards, leaflets, invitations and so on, it is quite possible that the final pages have been lost, but it is also possible that she was overwhelmed by news from home. Six-year-old Kenneth was desperately ill with pneumonia. Did Ida get this news? It would have been difficult for a telegram to reach her while she was travelling around, but she would have been contactable at the Parsons' house. It will have been a hard decision for Hugh MacLean to make as to whether he should contact her, since there was nothing she could do but worry.

She sailed for home on Tuesday 23rd March and perhaps she was kept informed of Kenneth's condition through the ship's telegraph. Kenneth remembered later that he was just recovering when his mother returned home, and that 'the drug-taking, unpleasant night nurse' who had been looking after him was sacked by her on the spot. Kenneth was only five, so his later recollection may not have been entirely accurate; it is hard to believe that Hugh MacLean and Kenneth's devoted nanny, who continued to be part of their family life for many years, would have allowed an unpleasant or incompetent nurse to care for him. It is easy, though, to imagine Ida, exhausted and distraught as she must have been, venting her anguish on the hapless woman.

Whether or not Ida felt that the trip had been worth the frustrations, exhaustion and anxiety, the IFUW flourished in the years that followed. Fundraising, though, got off to a slow start. It was 1923 before Ida, as Chair of the Funding Committee, felt able to come up with a scheme for the foundation of international fellowships and grants. The

American Federation had been funding such grants since the 1890s and Ida knew very well how much her own career had benefited from the Beit award and from the Ellen Richards prize. There was a powerful conviction among the founders of the IFUW that there was a particular need to fund women academics to travel, study and work abroad, and that this was essential in equipping them to compete on equal terms with men for academic posts. They were only too aware that although such funding was in theory available to both men and women, the model for funding travel abroad had a strong male bias. The Rockefeller Foundation of New York City and the National Research Council defined their ideal candidates for travel fellowships as 'bright, young men'. That perception had to be challenged. Ellen Gleditsch, a member of the International Fund Appeal Committee, underlined the need for giving women the opportunity to work abroad:

> 'Research demands sacrifices, economic and personal. If we want women to do research work we must give young women the opportunity of advanced study in their own country and in other countries. In fact, research in science will nearly always, and research in arts very often, necessitate years of study at foreign universities. I need not dwell on this; it is known and recognized by us all.'[15]

Gleditsch was a radiochemist and knew what she was talking about. Funded by a Norwegian research fellowship, she had worked in Paris in Marie Curie's laboratory.

The International Fund Appeal Committee, with Ida in the chair, initially came up with an ambitious aim to raise one million dollars in order to provide women with about

---

15 'The Need and Value of International Fellowship for Research' by Ellen Gleditsch (IFUW, file 71) p20.

thirty fellowships per year. Functioning as an endowment fund, the income would allow funding fellowships of different values. This was proposed at the third IFUW conference in Christiania (about to be renamed Oslo) in 1924, but among Ida's papers is a rather sad document – the rough draft, with a great deal of crossing out, of the speech she planned to deliver to the fourth IFUW conference in Amsterdam in 1926:

> 'When the resolution was adopted by the 3ʳᵈ Congress at Christiania to establish a million-dollar endowment Fund, the income of which was to be used for providing Fellowships, difficulties were anticipated which have proved to be very real ones. The Appeal Committee is however very glad to be able to report that a start has been made & that $10,500 or £2,100 have been collected. The difficulties facing us have been of various kinds...'

Europe was still poor after the war and national clubs had their own priorities. No award could be given until two years' time at the earliest, and though Ida put as positive a spin on the situation as she could, she ended her draft with a rather desperate selection of inspirational phrases with which she might round off:

> 'Women with brains for our ambassadors'.

> 'Merchants of light'.

> 'high standard of original scholarship which has taught her an appreciation of the difficulty of trying to find out what is the truth and which cannot be attained without imagination'.

> 'Community Service'.

She was making the best of quite a bad job and one has to be impressed by the effort.

She was not defeated. She was determined that the money should be raised somehow, and decided to propose the model suggested by the Dutch Federation, that each national federation should make an appeal for people to contribute one day's earnings to the fund. Interviewed in *The Times* after the conference, she presented a less ambitious scheme than the original million pounds; £120,000 was now the aim, with an interim aim of £26,000 for four scholarships in two years' time. The aims had become much more modest, but she was pragmatic and, in the event, a combination of strategies, including fundraising events and appeals to individual donors, raised the money that was needed. In 1928, the first international fellowship was awarded, and shortly after the American branch endowed several other international fellowships. In all, between 1928 and the outbreak of World War II, the IFUW awarded thirty-three international fellowships and nine grants for aid in research to academic women of seventeen different nationalities. Each of those had the potential to be career-changing.

As if the demands of the IFUW were not enough, Ida was still taking a lead in the running of the BFUW, which had embarked on a hugely ambitious project – the purchase of Crosby Hall in Cheyne Walk, Chelsea, and the building of new residential accommodation round it for women students from abroad studying in London. A programme for a run of performances (24th–27th March 1926) of a new play, *Sir Thomas More*, to raise funds for the project gives a lively, succinct account of Crosby Hall's chequered history:

'The Hall which forms the setting of this play was built in Bishopsgate in 1466 by Sir John Crosby a distinguished *diplomat and soldier who is, however, chiefly remembered by this fine model of 15th Century architecture, to which he gives his name. In 1483, Crosby Place was occupied by Richard, Duke of Gloucester, and it was here he proclaimed himself King of England, as recorded by Shakespeare in "Richard III". After various less distinguished tenancies, Crosby Place was rented in 1519 by Sir Thomas More and purchased by him in 1523. Probably Margaret Roper's marriage feast took place in this very hall... Many other distinguished persons, including Sir Philip Sidney's beautiful sister, the Countess of Pembroke, occupied Crosby Place after the death of Sir Thomas More; but the heyday of its glory declined in the 17th Century and it was no longer used as a private residence. Terrible indignities were offered to the beautiful building, until in 1831 Miss Maria Hackett took over the lease and did her best to restore its beauty. After various vicissitudes the Hall was purchased by a bank in 1907 and it was intended to pull it down and erect other buildings on the site. A Preservation committee was formed under the chairmanship of Sir Vezey Strong, and enough money was raised to move the whole building, stone by stone from Bishopsgate to its present site, Sir Thomas More's garden in Chelsea. In 1922, the Federation of University Women decided, if enough money could be raised, to buy the site and the Hall and to build round it a residential wing for women students of all nations. £33,000 has been already raised for this purpose, but £17,000 more is needed.'*

Both the project and the fundraiser have Ida's fingerprints all over them, one feels: a bold, high-profile undertaking, funded by women for women, to provide quality accommodation; and a perfectly judged theatrical event – a play by a woman (Ruth

Bray) about the hall's most famous former owner and the original owner of the land on which the building now stood. (It was also situated in Ida's home territory – in Chelsea, where she was now living, and just along the river from the Lister Institute.) Whoever it was who wrote the history of the hall crafted her narrative to emphasise the building's association with remarkable women, too – not only Maria Hackett, who tried to rescue and restore it, but also Margaret Roper, Thomas More's famously well-educated daughter and the Countess of Pembroke, neé Mary Sidney, a distinguished Renaissance classicist, poet and patron of literature and the theatre.

The project was a major commitment for Ida during 1926 and 1927. She kept the programme for the visit to the site on 17th November 1926 of the young Duchess of York (later Queen Elizabeth, wife of George VI). The duchess unveiled a commemorative tablet at the hall. (In hindsight, the choice of the duchess to celebrate an advance in women's education may have seemed ironic, since her own daughters complained that their education was quite inadequate!) Much of the responsibility for this occasion was taken by Winifred Cullis, who was president of the BFUW, vice-president of the IFUW and director of the Crosby Hall Association. The opening of the hall the following June involved a great deal of razzmatazz, with a host of distinguished guests, including a bevy of foreign diplomats, speeches, prayers, blessings, music, a reception and further festivities in the evening. Ida was among the selected guests who were presented to Queen Mary, who performed the official opening. The hall continued to provide accommodation for women students for nearly forty years. During the Second World War, the BFUW handed it over to the Greater London Council for war use and when the GLC was abolished in 1985, the hall was sold to a private buyer.

Ida and Winifred Cullis hardly had time to draw breath after the grand opening before they were off for a ten-day trip to Vienna for a council meeting of the IFUW – a meeting which nearly failed to take place because of serious political disturbances in Vienna in the week before:

'21–30 July I had arranged to travel out to Vienna with Winifred Cullis for the 11th Council Meeting of the IFUW. On Friday July 15th a demonstration was held outside the Law Courts of Vienna (Palais de Justice) to protest against the acquittal of some reactionaries (Fascists) who had killed a socialist at some meeting. The Communists used the occasion to promote revolution and very serious fighting occurred. A general strike followed and telegraphic communications and trains ceased.

By the following Wednesday, order was restored and telegrams received and having received the assurance of the Austrian Minister that all was quiet, on Thursday we left, arriving via Ostend and Wurzburg late on Saturday night (23rd). On the previous Wednesday and Thursday there had been 100 burials of those killed in street fighting but the funerals had passed off without disturbance. The University, which is very reactionary and therefore unpopular, had been attacked but the doors had been closed and it had escaped… We could only be admitted to the back door of the University with a pass, the door being always guarded with policemen and soldiers.'

This does not sound like an encouraging ambience for a meeting, but she continued:

'The meeting went off excellently. The open meeting was excellent, especially a speech by Dr von Zahn Harnack

on the Fellowship scheme of the Federation. The two most live moments of the congress were the discussion on the languages to be used at the conference, the use of German in discussion as well as French and English being eventually admitted, and (2) the suggestion that an International Cookery Book should be sold in England and America under the auspices of the IFUW, the profits to be given to the Fellowship Scheme. This aroused violent opposition from all the European university women except the French representative, on the plea that it would injure the standing of University Women, a point of view that the American representative found very difficult to understand.'

The difference of view between the European and the American members is an interesting one, and debate about whether women undermine their cause by linking themselves in any way to the domestic is a familiar one even now. Ida was no cook and may have joined in the opposition to the cookery book, but she enjoyed her food in Vienna, as she always did:

'We ate Wien Schnitzel and café melange especially good at the cellars of the Rathaus, dined at Coblenz where the British representative entertained the others to dinner looking over Vienna, dined in the Prater and with the Kurandas.'

And then:

'Finally we returned, loving Vienna and the Austrians very much and regretting we had ever found ourselves as enemies. Back to London with Winifred Cullis and was met by the family at Liverpool St at 9.30 on Saturday night July 30.'

It was a tradition that Ida and Hugh had established that, whenever she had been away, he brought the children to meet her on her return, no matter how late it was.

CHAPTER SEVEN

A GOOD TIME FOR MY PARENTS: HOME AND WORK

1919–1929

WRITING ABOUT THE 1920S, THE PERIOD OF HER childhood, Barbara MacLean sketches a picture of a happy, successful, active, prosperous couple, devoted to each other and to their children, both doing well in their careers and becoming figures in public life, with time and money for hobbies, cultural pursuits, and holidays. The picture is fleshed out in Ida's scrapbooks, which bulge with evidence of Hugh's and the children's pursuits and successes, as well as of her own busy work life. Ida kept one of their bespoke Christmas cards for 1926, which carries a picture of a classic sailing boat and the message, 'Hope guide your life and pleasure fill its sails'. The source of the quote (which they wrongly attribute to Shakespeare) is obscure, but it distils perfectly the mood of cheerful optimism and enjoyment of life that predominated in her diaries.

To take the work first, although the BFUW and IFUW were taking up a good deal of her time, her research was flourishing too. The *Biochemical Journal* archives show that between 1920 and 1929, she was an author of fifteen research papers.[16] There was no year in which she did not publish a paper, and she ended the decade in a flurry of activity: two papers in 1928 and three in 1929. Starting in 1920 with a paper entitled simply 'The Nature of Yeast Fat',[17] she worked on this material for the next ten years, writing papers on the metabolism of fat, on vitamins in fat, and on carbohydrate and fat. She is named as the sole author on two papers and first author on five more. It is very striking to see how much of her collaborative work was done with other women; in fact, all but two of her collaborative papers in that period were co-authored with women: three with Dorothy Hoffert (a former chemistry teacher who had moved into research work during the war), two with Ethel Thomas (head of the biology department at University College, Leicester), two with Margaret (Margot) Hume and Hannah Henderson Smith (with whom she continued to publish well into the 1930s), and others with Ethel Luce, Edith Clenshaw, Marion Battle and Dorothy Collison. Ida and Dorothy Hoffert followed up their 1926 paper with a presentation at a Biochemical Society meeting, where they spoke on 'The Synthesis of Fat by the Living Organism'. At the same meeting, Harriette Chick, Ida's colleague at the Lister, spoke on 'Sources of Error in the Biological Method of Investigating Fat-soluble Vitamins'. The Biochemical Society's decision to admit women as members almost from the outset was translating into women members' very active involvement.

The sinister explanation for this almost exclusive preference for working with other women would be that a lot of men were unwilling to work with a woman, and that may

---

16 A complete list of Ida's papers in the *Biochemical Journal* is to be found in Appendix III.

17 *Biochemical Journal* 'The Nature of Yeast Fat' by Ida Smedley-Ma-cLean, Ethel Mary Thomas, July 01 1920.

have been the case at that stage, but given the ease with which she moved in this world and the evident respect she enjoyed from male colleagues, it seems more likely that it was her conscious choice to work with women – a continuation of her general strategy of fostering female self-help in both formal and informal ways. She was happy to work in a mostly male environment, and to take her place in the mostly male clubs of the Chemical and Biochemical societies, but she relied at the same time on parallel female networks and used them to further her own career and those of her women colleagues.

She also published jointly with Hugh – not a paper in the *Biochemical Journal* but a book – a monograph entitled *Lecithin and Allied Substances – the Lipins*[18] in the series *Monographs on Biochemistry*, of which Ida's early champion, Gowland Hopkins, was one of the editors.

Hugh was having a highly successful time, and Ida was clearly proud of him, keeping a sheaf of newspaper cuttings about his flourishing research. This from the *Evening Standard* for 29th April 1926 gives a good account of his breakthrough in the treatment of diabetes and other diseases, and of his success in attracting funding for state-of-the-art facilities at St Thomas's. Headlined 'Science and the Fat Man – seeking a remedy at St. Thomas's – diet and disease', it continues:

---

18 *Lecithin and Allied Substances – the Lipins* by Hugh MacLean and Ida Smedley-MacLean (Longman's, Green & Co, 1927).
The contents of the book are summarised on the flyer as follows:
Contents: Chapter 1 Introduction & Nomenclature p1; Chapter II The chemistry of the phospholipins (phosphatides) – lecithin, kephalin, sphingomyelin p21; Chapter III The occurrence, methods of extraction, isolation and purification of the phospholipins p67; Chapter IV The galactolipins (cerebrosides) – phrenosin, kerasin and nervon p91; Chapter V Alleged lipins – protagon, cuorin, carnaubon, paranucleo-protagon, jecorin and other insufficiently characterised substances p124; Chapter VI Plant lipins p153; Chapter VII The function of lipins – Lipins from the biological standpoint p167; Bibliography p189; Index p217.

'Important results bearing upon the relationship of food to disease are looked for when the new laboratories about to be built in connection with the medical school of St Thomas's Hospital are in full swing. Hitherto, the research work, conducted under the control of Prof MacLean, has been considerably handicapped by lack of suitable accommodation. The new structure will replace Army huts that have been in use within the hospital grounds for the past ten years. "The work of building will start forthwith" said a medical authority of the hospital to an Evening Standard representative today "now that the necessary funds have been provided through the grant of £15,000 from the Rockefeller Foundation to supplement the £15,000 already set aside for this purpose. One section of the new Department will be set aside solely for the use of students and post-graduates coming from abroad. Professor MacLean has been particularly interested in the study of diet as affecting disease and… digestive disturbances. The work entails considerable expenditure and experiments have generally been seriously handicapped by the lack of sufficient funds which it is hoped will be forthcoming in generous measure to subsidise the work of the new department. The importance of digestion and diet upon problems of health is only gradually coming to be realised… the question of malnutrition and obesity is one of the problems to be investigated.'

A second article, the next day, headlined Hugh as 'the hero of the silent biochemical battle' and gave a detailed account of his ground-breaking work in using insulin to treat diabetes.

Ida and Hugh were by this time what would now be called a 'power couple', each successful and increasingly well known in their own right but also supporting and enhancing one another's careers. There were other couples among their contemporaries in biochemistry – Mary and Otto Rosenheim, Muriel and Hugh Onslow, Gertrude and Robert Robinson, for example – but no other couple where the woman had her own independent field of work. Ida's papers are full of invitations to and programmes for prestigious events: there is an invitation to a Buckingham Palace garden party on 7th March 1924 (it is addressed to 'Mr and Mrs Hugh MacLean' – the Lord Chamberlain clearly had no truck with academic titles). They were guests at the top table at a dinner celebrating the golden wedding of the Marquis and Marchioness of Aberdeen and Temair (philanthropists and supporters of good causes), and at two significant academic dinners. The first of these was a dinner on 8th October 1926 in the hall of Emmanuel College, Cambridge on the occasion of the presentation of Sir Frederick Gowland Hopkins's portrait to the Dunn Institute of Biochemistry. The seating plan in the programme shows Ida seated immediately opposite Gowland Hopkins himself. The top table stars included geneticist J.B.S. Haldane, and future Nobel laureate 'Harry' Quastel. Gowland Hopkins's Cambridge laboratory attracted women researchers, and the list of women guests reads as a roll call of Ida's most distinguished female contemporaries: Harriette Chick; Marjory Stephenson (one of the first two women to be elected a Fellow of the Royal Society); Cambridge geneticist Muriel Wheldale (the Hon. Mrs Onslow); pioneering protein scientist Dorothy Jordan Lloyd; Australian microbiologist June Lascelles; and Dorothy (Moyle) Needham, physiologist, Cambridge Fellow and human rights campaigner. Also present were Gowland Hopkins's daughters: Barbara, herself a biochemist, and sixteen-year-old Jacquetta, later the archaeologist Jacquetta Hawkes. It was a gathering that paid appropriate tribute to Gowland Hopkins and Ida must have been delighted to be in a place of honour opposite the man whose recommendation had done much to win her the fellowship that launched her career.

There is, however, a programme for a second dinner which may have given her even more satisfaction. Dated 15th December the following year (1927), it gives the details of a Jubilee Banquet of the Institute of Chemistry at the Wharncliffe rooms, Hotel Great Central, Marylebone. This was a huge dinner with more than 500 participants and the table plan shows Ida seated on the top table. She was there as the recently elected Chairman of the Biochemical Society. She had been on the council of the society since 1920 and was now its first woman chairman – a significant achievement. She was flanked by Gowland Hopkins representing the Royal College of Physicians and Prof George Barger representing the Royal Society of Edinburgh. Elsewhere on the top table was Ernest Rutherford, President of the Royal Society, and Ida's early London research supervisor, Henry Armstrong – the man whose vigorous opposition to women in the Chemical Society had been instrumental in keeping them out for so long. Ida must surely have felt a sense of triumph to find herself sitting with him in this distinguished company, her position recognised as the chairman of the Chemical Society's younger and more forward-looking sister society. A sweet moment, surely.

The grand occasions were not all academic. Ida kept a programme, dated 4th March 1927, for 'A Farewell Luncheon to His Excellency the Italian ambassador & the Marchesa della Torretta'. Many hostesses are listed, including Ida, and she has annotated the guest list: 'Colonello & Signora Coppi, Cap di Vascello Farina, my neighbours'. The MacLean family's move in 1923 across the river from their flat in Battersea to a family house in Chelsea had taken them into smart company. A photograph of Elm Park Gardens in the 1920s shows a very fine terrace of four-storey houses with deep bay windows and

2 Elm Park Gardens, Chelsea

ornate stonework. They were houses that would have involved an enormous amount of domestic work. Barbara describes the house and the domestic arrangements as follows:

'In the basement there was a kitchen, scullery and pantry, and on the ground floor there was a dining room and another room, converted to my father's chemistry laboratory. On the first floor there was a lounge, spare bedroom and bathroom and above this were bedrooms for my parents, myself and Kenneth. On the top floor there was a playroom, a bedroom for the senior staff

and a separate bedroom shared by two other staff. They
employed a parlour maid, who served food, a housemaid
who carried out housework and lit the fires, a cook and my
father's batman from the First World War, Field, who was
his driver and carried out other duties as needed.'

Ida was free from everyday domestic chores, but the staff
had to be managed, of course, and recruited – housemaids
came and went unpredictably and the search for new ones is a
running theme in the diaries.

She was coming to be regarded as something of a pundit
on academic matters. Among her papers there are two letters
from the editor of the *Morning Post*, asking for her views on
university issues. One of the subjects was an article by H.G.
Wells in an American journal, which predicted the demise of
the elite universities – Oxford, Cambridge and the American
Ivy League colleges – and the other was a speech made (in
Latin) by the retiring Vice-Chancellor of Oxford, Dr Joseph
Wells, which covered familiar reactionary ground – complaints
about the numbers of tourists in Oxford, the iniquities of the
General Strike and so on – and included the view that:

'*While I am anxious to see an increase in number of our*
students, I must beg for a limit to be placed by Statute
to the number of women studying at Oxford. I did my
utmost to secure the admission of women to degrees, nor
do I regret it. But who foresaw, at that time, that one-fifth
of our students would soon be women? Unless a legal limit
is enforced, their number will steadily increase.'

It was disappointing to find that although Ida responded (the
editor wrote to thank her), she did not keep a copy of her
reply!

She was still heavily involved in the running of the Lyceum clubs. Her papers are full of programmes for dinners and talks, and they include the typed text of a brief speech she herself gave on 8th February 1927 at a Lyceum club debate on the motion, '*That Woman's happiness is dependent on her personal relationships*', with Ida opposing. Her speech summed up her deep personal convictions about the importance to women of work, of autonomy and of self-respect:

> '*It is quite true that their personal relationships contribute very largely to the happiness of both men and women. But that is a very different thing from assuming that women are in some special way entirely dependent for their happiness on their personal relationships. I am going to leave out of account those tempestuous passions which come to both men and women generally for brief periods and which, on the whole, probably contribute more to the sorrow of life. Samuel Butler defines happiness by saying that we are happy when we don't know that we are miserable, very much in the same way that when we are healthy, we don't know that we have a body. We only know it when we are ill and we become conscious of the existence of various parts of our body which normally never attract our attention.*
>
> *The whole of the feminist movement, the tremendous change which has taken place in the position of women during the last 50 years has been based on two factors, one an economic one, the other the recognition that to be happy you cannot afford to put yourself entirely at the mercy of circumstances over which you have no control. You must have some interest in life – religion, career, occupation or work. Something which you can try and achieve as well as your personal relationships. A woman needs "… some work or some interest of her own into which she can*

throw herself over and over again…"(Trollope, Garden of Eden). If, in pursuing the interest or occupation you can weave in your personal relationships both sides of your life will gain. Even the fact that you are not utterly dependent on those personal relationships is going to enormously improve your chances of establishing those relations on a satisfactory basis. Nothing is more likely to endanger the relations than the fact that the other person knows that you are utterly dependent on them.'

This was not to say that personal relationships were of secondary importance to her. Her friendships were loyal and longstanding, she maintained affectionate contact with the wider family, she was a loyal sister, a devoted wife and a proud and loving mother. It is striking to see how intermingled with evidence of work successes and public status are the mementoes of family life: holiday snaps, pantomime programmes, Christmas memorabilia, records of the children's illnesses and successes, and evidence of their creative skills and ideas. It is a joyous life, though not without its anxieties, of course – even its terrors. Between 24th February and 6th March 1924, nine-year-old Kenneth was in hospital with measles. He must have had complications. Pneumonia was a common complication and Kenneth was prone to chest infections; without antibiotics, this could have been fatal. Ida kept a record of his temperature readings, which peaked at 104.6°F on the night of 29th February/1st March. She wrote nothing else during this period, but the temperature chart speaks for itself. Elsewhere in Ida's memorabilia, Kenneth emerges as a robust, confident, clever and inventive boy, witty and entertaining. He enjoyed writing. Ida kept a rather good limerick, intended for a competition in *Time and Tide* in January 1926:

"'There once was a cleric whose face
Bore of kindness and love not a trace,
He feigned to be good,
But 'twas well understood
He belonged to the Hypocrite race."
Kenneth MacLean 2, Elm Park Gardens Chelsea SW10.'

I wondered whether he had been influenced by his grandfather's views on religion. The poem is annotated, *'Unfortunately, at the last moment the coupon page was found to be burnt & he couldn't send in'*. There were moments of inefficiency even in Ida's formidably competent life.

And Barbara's achievements are recorded too: *'Barbara was head of her class for the first time this week & has a badge as prefect & a prize'*. Both the children exhibited the same confidence in dealing with adults as Ida and her siblings learnt from their parents, and, like the Smedleys, Hugh and Ida included the children in their own hobbies and enthusiasms. There is a cricket scorecard for the final innings of the Surrey 2ⁿᵈ XI vs Wiltshire at the Oval, annotated, *'A peaceful Whit Monday at the Oval with Barbie & Ken seeing 2ⁿᵈ class cricket. Hugh drove down to Guildford to see a case there'* – work was never far away. Family holidays were spent in Scotland, where Hugh could indulge his passions for shooting, fishing and golf, and Ida and Kenneth joined dutifully in the golf, at least. There are several golf cards from Elgin and Moray golf clubs and Barbara, who sounds less than delighted by these Scottish holidays, writes that:

'Every August we all went up to Scotland where my father shot at Knockando in Strathspey, an estate owned by Lord Woolavington, a former patient who had become a friend, while my mother and my brother played golf on

various local links. I went with them but, too young to join
in their pursuits, occupied myself as best I could.'

These Scottish holidays and the outdoor pursuits that went with them were vitally important to Hugh, and the family looks cheerful enough in the holiday snapshots.

The only obvious blight on the happiness and success of these years was the death of Ida's mother and the consequences that followed for her father. Ida wrote nothing about this; she was not yet in the habit of confiding private feelings to her records. Later, she wrote movingly about her father's death and about Connie's final illness and death, but the only indication of her mother's death is a black-edged printed card, dated 13th February 1923, with a formal message from '*Mr W.T. Smedley and family*' thanking friends for their condolences on their sad loss. Anne Smedley's death must have been a blow to Ida. From her determination to send her to the best possible school, her inclusion of her daughters in her own social and cultural life, and her encouragement to study at Newnham, to the home she provided for her in London until her marriage, she had offered outstanding support to a daughter pursuing an unconventional career. And Barbara makes it clear that she was a much-loved grandmother. She and Kenneth saw their grandparents often at their home in Cheyne Walk, where her grandmother was always ready with 'imaginative games'. With her children still young, Ida lost invaluable support from her wise and generous mother.

Ida and Hugh's move from Battersea to Chelsea in 1923 may have been partly with a view to being close to Ida's father but, if so, he had other ideas. He had bought a large house at Limpley Stoke near Bath, overlooking the River Avon, and two years after his wife's death he moved there, although he had not yet retired from running Roneo and needed to make frequent trips to London. He took with him to the new house Gertrude Vickers, who had started working for the Smedleys as a young kitchen maid and had become their housekeeper in Cheyne Walk. Barbara writes as follows:

> 'Gertrude Vickers went with him and, shortly afterwards, began working on him to marry her. We now believe that my grandfather had had an earlier relationship with her; he was fond of the ladies. My Smedley cousins, then living at Limpley Stoke, were convinced that a so-called nephew named Jack, whom Gertrude brought to play with them, was in fact her and my grandfather's son. In 1927 my grandfather submitted to Gertrude's pressure and married her. This was a considerable shock to his children who, with good reason, had never liked Gertrude and were not prepared to accept her. A major rift accordingly developed between my grandfather and his family.'

This is the first hint of scandal in the model relationships of the Smedleys, although Barbara's comment that William Smedley *'was fond of the ladies'* may signify that she was aware that there had been other indiscretions. A rift of this sort must have been deeply undermining to a family that had prided itself on its affectionate, tolerant, supportive relationships. The rights and wrongs of the situation are impossible to assess. Barbara, who was only a child at the time, must, to some extent, have been reporting her parents' views (and perhaps those of the cousins she mentions, Billy's children), but was Gertrude *'a virago'*, as Barbara asserts? Or were the Smedley children simply being snobbish about their father marrying a former kitchen maid? One feels that they would have needed very good reasons to allow the marriage to destroy a family with such a history of affection for and pride in one another, and letters between Ida and her father in the early 1930s suggest that she, at least, still felt close to him and he was offering her support in a difficult time. But William Smedley changed his will ten months before he died in 1934, leaving his entire fortune to Gertrude. Barbara casts doubt on the theory that Gertrude's nephew Jack was in fact her son when she notes that when Gertrude died, she left him only a hundred pounds, leaving larger sums to other members of her family.

Barbara mentions her cousins living in Limpley Stoke, and William Smedley's decision to move there is partly explained by the fact that Billy was running the Hydro Hotel there. Billy, handsome and charming but with no financial acumen and, as his final report from University College School London expressed it, 'lacking moral backbone', never managed to stand on his own feet financially. Initially, his father employed him in his business, then he acquitted himself well during the war, fighting throughout in the Artists' Rifles. After the war, his father set him up to run a poultry farm (a popular occupation for ex-officers at the time) and then, when that bored him, was persuaded to buy the Hydro Hotel in Limpley Stoke and appoint him manager. Perhaps William Smedley felt he needed to be close at hand to keep an eye on his investment.

Billy certainly had the panache to run a smart hotel. Grace's Guide for 1927 advertises the hotel as, 'A Country Hotel that all motorists can afford and where the excellence of the cooking is remarkable'. In its fifteen acres of wooded land overlooking the Limpley Stoke Valley, it offered 'Croquet, Clock Golf, Billiards, Boating and Wireless'. The Hydro, we learn, was equipped for electrical and Turkish baths. The tariff was to be obtained from W.H. Smedley, who did not describe himself as anything so mundane as a manager, but as the 'Director'. There is also, among Ida's papers, an expensively printed menu for Christmas lunch at the hotel in 1926. I assume that she,

Hugh and the children spent Christmas 1926 there. Perhaps that was a way of seeing her father over the Christmas period without being under Gertrude's roof.

The year 1926 had been triumphant in many ways, and there was more happiness and success to come in the rest of the decade. Hugh's work was very much in the news again – the press and the public found the subject of diet and exercise as interesting then as they do now – and Ida kept a growing bundle of newspaper cuttings relating to his work. His growing fame led to an invitation to undertake an extended lecture tour in Australia in August 1929. The centrepiece of the tour was the Australasian Medical Congress in Sydney, where he gave a lecture, but before that he travelled around the Melbourne and Sydney area, lecturing to doctors and postgraduate students. He wrote a diary of his tour, which was probably intended for Ida and the children, and which Ida kept among her papers. It compares interestingly with Ida's diary of her US lecture tour. They share the same eager appetite for the new and strange, and the same desire to do well and be appreciated, but Hugh's diary does not have Ida's flashes of humour, nor her resilience. His lectures were very well received but he was more anxious than Ida and felt the strain of the demands on him and of the separation from 'the little family' from the start. He arrived in Melbourne on 9th August, and by 12th he was already regretting not being up in Scotland for the start of the grouse-shooting season. Australia suited him, in that he was given multiple opportunities for shooting, fishing and playing golf, but it also exhausted him, and he pined for Ida and the children, who had taken the opportunity of the break from the annual stay in Scotland to holiday in France and Switzerland, but sent regular telegrams assuring him that they were well. His final diary entry before boarding a ship for home summarises his feelings:

'Tuesday Sep 19th 1929. Melbourne

The great day on which I set out for home has arrived at last. I had a most excellent time in Australia, and everybody says that the lectures were a great success. The continuous run of lunches and dinners has been somewhat of a strain and now that all is finished (I think successfully) I am very glad to get away. Several times during the past 6 weeks I have longed for the day on which I could feel that my Australian visit was finished for after all it was a time of some responsibility and anxiety.'

Kenneth, in his obituary of his father in Munk's Roll, suggests that this tour, in place of his usual month of relaxation in Scotland, sowed the seeds of the illness that attacked him the following year. This was the family's explanation for his breakdown and Barbara too cites this as the reason why, as she puts it, their *'satisfactory life came to an end'*.

CHAPTER EIGHT

THIS SATISFACTORY LIFE CAME TO AN END

1930–1931

In 1930, Ida began to write a daily journal, starting off in a series of Roneo indexed diaries, produced by her father's company. Some of these (including the 1930 diary) have 'DR IDA MACLEAN' embossed in gold on them, and it is likely that they were gifts from Ida's father, an indication that the family breach, between the two of them, at least, was not as absolute as Barbara felt it had been.

At the beginning of the year, there seems to have been no sign of the illness that would attack Hugh. He went on fishing and shooting trips to Lavington in Wiltshire and to Meopham in Kent, as well as playing golf on various outer London courses, and he attended dinners at his various clubs, as well as accompanying Ida to Biochemical Society dinners. Ida herself was as busy as ever: entries for the first three months of the year alone record thirteen Lyceum Club meetings and events, nine Biochemical Society meetings and twenty BFUW meetings – mainly concerned with the management of Crosby Hall, which was turning out to be a major responsibility. She also recorded thirty lunch or dinner engagements over that period. These were sometimes simply catching up with friends and family but were more often networking sessions or informal meetings with fellow Lyceum Club and BFUW committee members. Recording where and with whom she ate lunch, tea and dinner became a habit which she continued for the rest of her life. In addition, in the memorandum pages at the front of the diary, she listed the names of forty guests she planned to invite to formal dinners and receptions in the coming year.

One day selected from these three months gives a flavour of the way she could pack a day. Her entry for Thursday 9th January 1930 reads as follows:

'10.30–12.45 *Lister in the morning – made up solution of Drummonds carotene & took m. pt.*

1.15 Barbara called for me & we lunched at the Florence with the Women's Provisional Club. Edith Shackleton talked on dramatic critics.

Met Kenneth at Leicester Square Station & went to Kingsway Theatre to see

2.30 School for Scandal. Frank Collier & Angela Baddeley very good as Sir Peter & Lady Teazle – Asked for upper circle seats & were given front row of stalls where we saw rather too well.

Dined with Winnie 8 p.m.

Gave Hugh a barometer as part of his Christmas present.

At Winnie's met Miss Matheson of the BBC & Winifred Holtby & Mrs Bosanquet.'

A morning's work, lunch and a lecture, a matinee at the theatre and a dinner party in the evening. And the children, still on school holiday, were incorporated into her day. Her enjoyment of the children as companions is very evident from the diaries for this and the following years. Barbara was a rather grown-up twelve-year-old, now at St Paul's Girls' School in Hammersmith, and Kenneth was an enterprising fifteen-year-old at Westminster School, and she drew them into her life, as well as taking their own interests and activities seriously. She emerges from her diaries not only as a proud and affectionate mother, but as a facilitator. She not only introduced her children to the activities she loved – theatre, music, golf – but she also entered into their interests – watching cricket, encouraging their social activities and fostering the family talent for performance. There is an elegant, professionally printed programme for a homemade entertainment at the end of the school holiday in January 1930:

'*KENNETH S. MACLEAN*
WITH THE HELP OF THE MEMBERS
OF THE COMPANY
PRESENTS
MORE OR LESS

2 ELM PARK GARDENS SW10
14TH *JANUARY 1930*'

'*The company*', assembled by fifteen-year-old Kenneth, included not only Barbara and several of Kenneth's schoolfriends, but his eighteen-year-old cousin Oliver, Billy and Olive's son, who had come to work in London after leaving school. He was not living with the MacLeans, but Ida's diary entries record '*Oliver to dinner*' or '*to lunch*' frequently, and she was clearly keeping a motherly eye on him. He appears occasionally in the 1930 diary in lists of people to whom she has paid cheques, and she hosted his birthday celebration on 19th February. It is possible that he was working for his grandfather in the Roneo business, and this was how the printed programme was achieved. He went on to be much more successful than his father had been. He became a chartered accountant and during World War II he fought as a gunner and paratrooper, reaching the rank of Major and winning the Military Cross in 1944. After the war he became a successful businessman, as well as being a high-profile campaigner for economic liberalism and active in the Liberal Party. In 1930, however, it will have been his talent as a performer that Kenneth was interested in; Oliver not only had the Smedley performer's genes but those of his mother, who had been a professional actor before her marriage.

Devising and rehearsing the show was obviously the post-Christmas project for Kenneth and his friends before they went back to school, and Ida recorded the friends being at the house for lunch on most days. On the evening of the show itself, she entertained the performers' parents, together with Connie and Max and other friends of the family, to the 'revue' – a medley of song, dance, piano interludes and sketches – and to supper afterwards; there were twenty people, plus a separate list of the domestic staff who were included: 'Old Nannie, Charlie, Mrs Brown, Field & 3 Maids'. It was poignant to find these entries – evidence of the happy, family life that would end abruptly within a few months.

The months from April to June proceeded tranquilly, it seems. Ida continued to go to her lab; to attend committee meetings; to lunch and dine with friends, acquaintances and colleagues. Hugh was shooting and fishing at weekends, and also working extremely hard, combining his work at St Thomas's with seeing patients in his Harley Street practice and often travelling some distance to see patients in their homes.

For two weeks in April, the whole family went to stay at Minchinhampton in Gloucestershire, where Connie and Max had lived before the war. (There, they stayed with a Miss Bidmead at The Laburnums, Pinefarthing – an address with a powerful aura of Miss Marple about it.) From Minchinhampton, she went with the children to Bath to see her father at The Cliffe, his large house overlooking the River Avon. He sent his car to fetch Ida and the children, and they lunched with him and Gertrude – an effort was being made to heal the rift.

Ida was also supporting Billy and Olive. At some point when Billy was running the Hydro Hotel at Limpley Stoke, he and Olive parted, and it may have been during 1930. Ida saw each of them separately several times in the course of that year, and Olive's name appears frequently in her lists of letters written, so this may have been a difficult time for her. Billy was not always easy to stay in touch with; one diary entry reads, 'Asked Billy to dinner. No reply and didn't come.'

It was in late May that the first intimations of Hugh's ill health appeared. He started to suffer from severe gastric pain. Ironically, diet and the treatment of peptic ulcers was one of Hugh's medical specialisms. He diagnosed a stomach ulcer, started on a milk diet and seemed gradually to recover. Ida felt that he was well enough for her to go to the IFUW conference in Prague in July, but, unusually, she wrote nothing about the conference in her diary and returned early to make preparations for the annual trip to Scotland which, it was hoped, would restore Hugh to health.

In the event, the journey had quite the opposite result. They travelled by car, with Hugh and Field, the chauffeur, sharing the driving, and stayed overnight in Penrith, but as they drove on into Scotland the next day, Ida recorded, 'H v quiet and depressed. Field drove all the way.' They carried on with the holiday, staying with Hugh's brother, Andrew, on his farm near Inverness; visiting his mother, Barbara, now living in a nursing home nearby; and playing golf. Hugh went to Knockando to shoot, as usual, but Ida was worried about him, and on the third day of their visit she, Hugh and Kenneth drove to Aberdeen to see Ashley Mackintosh, a medical colleague, who found nothing wrong physically with Hugh. His physical health was not the issue, however, although his earlier gastric condition may have been a contributory factor to his depression, or another symptom of the stress he was feeling. In Ida's diary for 12ᵗʰ August, their day begins to sound like the holiday from hell:

> 'Tues Aug 12ᵗʰ 1930
> Knockando shoot.
> Very wet.
>
> Barbara Ken & I drove as far as Torres with Hugh on his way to Knockando – B & K beating me 2–1 – a moist round. Had lunch – an inadequate one at the Clubhouse during a terrific downpour & then Ken & I played a rather hopeless 16 holes – went down to the town shopped & had tea & were picked up by Hugh about 6.
>
> H shot well but was very depressed all day.'

Wet weather, hopeless golf and an inadequate lunch while they hung around waiting for Hugh, who had been too depressed to enjoy his shooting anyway. Even Ida's resolute good humour must have been put to the test.

By the following weekend, they had made the decision that she and Hugh should return to London to get treatment for him. They took the train down, leaving the children and Field in Inverness, and went to see a specialist, Dr Symonds, recommended by Ashley Mackintosh, in Wimpole Street the following day. Hugh was admitted to a nursing home and Ida slept by herself at Elm Park Gardens, the staff having been sent off on their holidays and the house shut up. There followed a frantic few days in which she 'haunted' (her word) employment agencies, looking for temporary domestic staff, as well as a nurse for Hugh. Mental hospitals were terrifying places in 1930, and Hugh wanted to be looked after at home. Ida did this as far as was possible, though there were periods in the course of the next four years when it was thought essential for him to be in a hospital or nursing home. Ida was never happy with that; she visited him constantly, pressing all the time for his return home. At this initial stage, finding domestic staff in London in August turned out to be the first hurdle. She spent the next few days alternating between spending time with Hugh at the nursing home, taking him for walks and chasing up domestic staff. By the Thursday she had a housekeeper and a cook, and on Friday she brought Hugh home, together with a nurse, hired from the staff at the nursing home.

The first week of caring for Hugh at home was a bumpy one. Ida was upset by the restrictions that Dr Symonds was making on the time she spent with Hugh; at first she was having lunch and dinner with him and spending the time between four and seven in the afternoon with him, but two days later:

'Symonds came 6.30. Symonds now refuses to let me have lunch & dinner with Hugh. I am only to see him from 4 to 7. This is after a long colloquy with the new nurse.'

It is not clear why these restrictions were being made. She decided that she wanted a second opinion and called in Dr Gordon Holmes:

'G.H. came, examined H & was exceedingly nice, thinks he ought to go to Penshurst to Ross & believes he will be at work again in 3 months.

H still convinced they're all wrong & he won't cure.'

Mental illness was an uncertain branch of medicine in 1930, with different practitioners holding radically different views on cause and treatment. Virginia Woolf, in her 1925 novel *Mrs Dalloway*, drew on her own experience of being treated for bipolar disorder to draw a savage picture of psychiatrists – authoritarian, arrogant and unfeeling. The doctors treating Hugh were clearly not like that (although, by an odd coincidence, Woolf names one of her doctors Dr Holmes) and Ida mostly found them *'very kind'*, but they may have expected a level of deference and acceptance that she was not willing to give.

Reading the diary, I could feel Ida's frustration: she could not simply give in and leave things to the experts. She was used to managing events, to solving problems and to moving fast. Her diary at this time consists of nothing but long lists of letters written (presumably cancelling, rearranging and generally putting her life on hold) and an obsessive record of the minutiae of Hugh's condition and treatment: his sleep patterns, what he ate and drank, his moods and how many grains of medinal he took. It must have been her scientist's instinct to record anything quantifiable as a foothold in the slippery world of mental illness. Hugh himself did not believe he could be cured but Ida seized on any sign of improvement: a fleeting smile, an attempted joke, a mention of something that had once interested him, even the fact that he had complained that his milk was too hot: *'1st time he has noticed temperature.'* Frail straws to be clutching at. *'Slightly better', 'much better', 'more like himself'* is a refrain that runs through the pages, only to be followed by disappointment.

The decision that Hugh should go down to Penshurst may have been dictated by the return of Kenneth and Barbara from Scotland for the start of the school term. There was a view that the children should not be in the house while Hugh was being nursed there. This may have been partly because they would disturb him, but the main reason was that his behaviour at this stage was alarming. He seems to have been haunted by ideas of guilt which related back to the Calvinist beliefs of his childhood. (I wondered whether the onset of the depression as soon as they arrived in Scotland was not coincidental, but somehow connected with childhood experiences.) Kenneth later told his children that he remembered all the blinds being drawn, throwing the house into gloom, and his father loudly proclaiming doom and damnation in his room. The imperative that the children should be kept away from him was so absolute that, when they arrived in London from Scotland on 16th September, Ida took them to a hotel '*and stayed the night with them as Hugh and the nurses were still at home*'.

The next day she took Hugh down to Penshurst. The hospital, run by Dr T.A. Ross, was the Ernest Cassel Hospital, founded by the philanthropist in 1919 for the treatment of traumatised ex-soldiers. Ross was a pioneering psychiatrist using psychotherapeutic rather than medicinal treatments and Ida liked him immediately: '*Dr Ross was very nice and thoroughly sensible*'. She was still being shut out, however; when she phoned for a progress report two days later, '*he'd rather I didn't go down for a day or two and try what a complete mental change can do*'. In the event, the results of the new treatment were deeply disappointing, and two weeks after Hugh's admission, Dr Ross phoned Ida to say that he was not at all well. Perhaps he had reported this to the MacLean's GP, Dr Jones, because he went to see Ida the same day and offered to have the children to stay with his family if she wanted

Hugh to come home. The Joneses were family friends – they had been guests at Kenneth's entertainment in January, and *'young Jones'* was a friend of Kenneth's. Hugh did come home the following week: *'very hopeless and rather apathetic, partly due to medinal – he has been having 13 grains nightly'*. So much for psychotherapeutic treatments.

The children had gone to stay with the Joneses in Upper Berkeley Street, three miles from Elm Park Gardens. Initially, Ida's attention was on Hugh, whose symptoms were constantly changing – not only a terrible sense of despair but panic attacks and breathlessness, trouble walking and a feeling of paralysis, sleeplessness and loss of appetite. There is no mention in her diary of work or of her usual round of committee meetings and other engagements. By late October, however, she started to re-engage with her life: she spent time at the Lister, went to meetings and fundraising events, and was involved again in her children's lives. She started, in fact, a period of the most extraordinary partitioning of each day between her work and public life, activities with the children and time spent with Hugh.

The most absorbing aspect of her work at this point was her engagement with the Vitamin Committee. This was a Medical Research Council initiative, involving biochemists who, like Ida, were working in the new field of vitamins – or 'vital amines'. Gowland Hopkins was awarded his Nobel prize as a result of his discovery, in 1912, of unknown factors in milk that were not fats, proteins or carbohydrates but proved to be essential to growth in young rats. By the early 1920s, these 'accessory factors' were being named vitamin A, and in January 1925, Ida published a paper, with Ethel Luce, on 'The Presence of Vitamin A in Yeast Fat',[19] following this up with another joint paper, in January 1928, on vitamins A and

---

19 *Biochemical Journal* 'The Presence of Vitamin A in Yeast Fat' by Ethel Marjorie Luce, Ida Smedley-MacLean, 01 January 1925.

D in yeast fat.[20] So, in working on vitamins, she was at the forefront of research, part of a vigorous team, with several of its members working at the Lister. Other members of the Vitamin Committee whom she mentions were:

+ Edward Mellanby (knighted in 1937), the first researcher to make the crucial discovery that rickets, the crippling bone disease which was rife among the urban poor, was caused by lack of vitamin D through lack of sunlight, and pioneer in the use of cod liver oil as a remedy.
+ K.H. Coward, a colleague of Mellanby's, who published prolifically on vitamin research.
+ Otto Rosenheim, an early refugee from antisemitism in Germany in the 1890s and a founding member of the Biochemical Society, working at King's College London on vitamin D.
+ Mary Christine Rosenheim, an early Newnham student who had been instrumental in having the Biochemical Society opened up to women.
+ John (Jack) Drummond (knighted in 1944), the first professor of biochemistry at University College London and the man who first isolated pure vitamin A.
+ Margaret Hume, who did pioneering work on malnutrition and bone disease. They were an impressive group and Ida felt honoured to be among them.

She published no papers in 1930 (the first time in over a decade when she had a year without a publication) but two papers came out in January the following year, one written jointly

---

20 *Biochemical Journal* 'The examination of yeast fat for the presence of vitamins A and D before irradiation and of vitamin D after irradiation' by Eleanor Margaret Hume, Hannah Henderson Smith, Ida Smedley-MacLean, 01 January 1928.

with Margaret Beavan Pearce,[21] which was a continuation of her work on fatty acids, and the other with Dorothy Collison, on lipoid matter extracted from spinach and cabbage leaves,[22] which suggests to me, as a layperson, that she was interesting herself in vitamin C as well. These papers were written, presumably, in the later part of 1930, even though they may have been writing up work done at an earlier stage.

The pattern of her days was, generally, work in the lab in the morning, time spent with Hugh in the afternoon, and time spent with the children in the evenings. BFUW, IFUW, Lyceum and other meetings were squeezed in at lunch times or late afternoon or at weekends. The children were having rather adult evenings – eating in restaurants or going to the theatre. Wanting to see them, unable to bring them home and not wanting to impose on the Joneses, Ida had few other options. Barbara was too young to understand properly what was happening to her father (she never really forgave him for the disruption to her childhood and had an uneasy relationship with him later on), but it is evident that Kenneth was a real support to his mother at this time. At nearly sixteen, he was old enough to go to and fro between Upper Berkeley Street and Elm Park Gardens on his own. He would sometimes call in to see his mother in the evenings, after his father was asleep. He also came over to see his father when Hugh asked to see him, and, as time went on, he took on the role of companion to his mother, going to the theatre with her, going for walks and playing golf. Ida arranged outings with the children – shopping and lunches

21 *Biochemical Journal* 'The Oxidation of Oleic Acid by Means of Hydrogen Peroxide' by Ida Smedley-MacLean, Margaret Sarah Beavan Pearce, January 01 1931.

22 *Biochemical Journal* 'The nature of the lipoid matter extracted from green leaves (spinach and cabbage)' by Dorothy Louisa Collison, Ida Smedley-MacLean, January 01 1931.

with Barbara, theatre, a pantomime and dinner with both of them – but one can see how, with Kenneth, outings shifted to his accompanying her, enabling her to carry on with the activities she enjoyed.

She must have been in need of companionship, because what is missing from the diary in these months is the record of all the lunches, teas and dinners which had punctuated her days so regularly up until Hugh's illness. With their blend of networking, informal business and catching up with friends, they had constituted her social life outside the family. Suddenly, these stopped. Something, of course, had to go if she was to spend the hours she felt she needed to spend with Hugh, and see her children, but it must have been an acute loss. In the weeks between 6th October and 15th December, she notes cancelled appointments on no less than twenty-two days, quite apart from invitations declined. That vigorous strand of her life, and the support it might have offered, had been cut off. One wonders who she was talking to. Connie would seem to have been too self-absorbed to be of much help, and there is no mention of meetings with old friends. She saw her oldest and closest friend, Winifred Cullis, seven times in the months from January to July, but not at all after that. Did Ida feel that Winifred, unmarried and without children, could not really understand or advise? Did the stigma of mental illness make discussing it outside the family impossible? Or was Ida so much in the habit of managing and making decisions that she simply could not ask for advice or help?

Barbara writes that: 'During this difficult time my mother was particularly hard hit by the rift with my grandfather, to whom she would normally have turned for sympathy and advice,' but the rift is not apparent at this point. On the weekend of 31st October to 3rd November, Ida, no doubt desperate for a break, took Kenneth to Minchinhampton (it must have been

Kenneth's half term). There they stayed at The Bear Hotel, played golf, phoned home frequently for updates on Hugh and, on the Sunday, went over to Bath to see Ida's father. Two days after their return home, Ida wrote a letter to her father (her letters to him were returned by Gertrude after his death and were kept with the diaries), in which she thanked him for the cheque he had given her. The affectionate letter is signed off with her family nickname, *Di*, and doesn't suggest estrangement, and the mention of the cheque suggests that William Smedley was ready with practical help, at least, to ease the practicalities of the complicated life that Ida and the family were leading.

Ida rarely raises the question of money in her diaries – she writes like a woman who has never really had to worry about it – but I did wonder how she managed the finances during this period. Hugh was not working at all and so was getting no income from his private practice. He did not formally resign from his post at St Thomas's until the following year, so he may still have been being paid something in the interim, but Ida was not yet being paid a salary as a full member of staff at the Lister but receiving research funding from the Department of Scientific and Industrial Research, which was unlikely to have been over-generous. And there were major medical expenses in these pre-NHS days: almost daily visits from Dr Jones and frequent visits from the psychiatrist, Dr Symonds, as well as two full-time nurses. I imagine that Ida must have been drawing on their savings, with no idea how long this situation would continue. It does seem likely that her father's cheque was a contribution to these expenses.

Barbara writes of her mother at this time '*remaining hopeful and cheerful throughout*', but Hugh continued to feel hopeless. Tucked into the diary, and dated by Ida '*16th November 1930*', is a note from Hugh written in pencil:

*'It is quite certain that I can never get better darling Ida.
Keep this as a remembrance of your loving Hugh.'*

His despair must have been heartbreaking, but Ida wrote
in her diary only that Kenneth came in to see them later and
had *'a very good interview'* with Hugh, and that she then went
back to the Joneses with him to see Barbara. Simply keeping
going seems to have been her strategy for coping.

December saw the fragile domestic arrangements become
unsustainable. When the Joneses offered to have the children
to stay, they may have had in mind Dr Ross's prediction that
Hugh would be back at work in three months, but they were
now into the fourth month with no prospect of improvement
and may have been feeling the strain. Ida realised that some
other arrangement would need to be made for the school
holidays – she could not expect the Joneses to have her children
at home with them all day. She started looking at flats to rent,
finding one in Earl's Court Road, about a mile from home.
The plan was that she and the children would live there during
the Christmas holidays, and this they did. On 18th December,
Ida gave a presentation on her work at the Lister, cancelled an
evening appointment and moved into the flat in Earl's Court
Road with the children.

She concluded her account of that day with, *'I began
reading* Evelina'. The novel *Evelina, or a History of a Young
Lady's Entrance into the World* by Fanny Burney is among the
earliest English novels, published in 1777. With its blend of
romance and social satire, it was a model for Jane Austen. This
sounds like a 'holiday read' for Ida, and she may have been
looking forward to these weeks as a sort of holiday – no doubt
hoping that the children would see it like that too. They were
without servants: *'Got our own breakfast'* she announced the
next day, and *'Shopped with children all morning, returning to*

flat for lunch & frying sausages & potatoes'. There was novelty in 'camping' at the flat, and the children went to Christmas parties and for outings with other families, as well as going with Ida to see a late nineteenth-century farce: *The Private Secretary* and *Toad of Toad Hall*. They also went to a Rural England conference, organised by their Aunt Connie, at which they were introduced to Richmal Crompton, author of the *Just William* books. They had as good a Christmas holiday as could be managed, ending with a stay in Cambridge with Beatrice Thomas in the New Year.

When they returned, it was to come back home. Ida now had fresh advice from a more senior consultant, who saw Hugh on 3rd January. He had the impossibly fictitious-sounding name of Sir Farquar Buzzard, but he had been mentioned by Dr Ashley Mackintosh, whom they had consulted in Aberdeen the previous August. In a cable to Ida on their return to London, he had informed her that Sir Farquar Buzzard was not available, but he could recommend Symonds, '*a very good man working for Buzzard*'. Now the great man himself came to give his opinion, and though Ida noted nothing more than that he visited, he may have encouraged her to live her life as normally as possible. And Hugh himself must have been in a better state. Through December she had already stopped recording the daily details of his condition, no longer noting his sleep patterns, his medication, his moods. Now, rather than sitting with him for long periods, she was taking him out for daily walks in Battersea Park, or for drives and walks in Richmond Park.

She returned to her vigorous work life, going regularly to her lab at the Lister in the mornings and participating in planning meetings. Her committee work picked up, including a new committee set up to oppose the abolition of university representation in the House of Commons. Oxford, Cambridge, London and the Scottish universities at this stage had their own Members of Parliament, but a 'manifesto' had been issued against this practice. A House of Commons committee had been set up to consider the question and Ida was asked to attend – a further indication of her public profile in academic affairs. The novelist John Buchan, who was the MP for the combined Scottish universities, was a member of the committee, as was Eleanor Rathbone, independent MP and women's rights campaigner.

Her social and cultural life returned too, to some extent. She was going to the monthly concerts conducted by Malcolm Sargent at the Courtauld Institute – Beethoven's Ninth Symphony in February and a Stravinsky concert in March – and she was at dinners and receptions at Crosby Hall. In March, the BFUW gave a dinner for women novelists: Rose Macaulay, best known for *The Towers of Trebizond*; Helen Ashton, now rediscovered by Persephone Press; Margaret Kennedy, whose bestselling novel *The Constant Nymph* was adapted as a successful play and film; and children's writer and prominent suffragist Evelyn Sharp.

This was a brave attempt at life as usual, but Hugh was still nowhere near his usual self. Dr Jones was still calling three or four times a week to see him, with regular visits from Dr Symonds and occasional ones from Sir Farquar Buzzard. Ida recorded their visits but no details about treatment or prognosis. It seems as though she had settled for a modus vivendi that they could all cope with and was trying to be content with that. She was having to take responsibility for everything, including a contentious issue that blew up connected with Hugh's work. Two diary entries read as follows:

'Sat Feb 28ᵗʰ 1931
Received packet of Stomach powder from Macleans with Hugh's name on. Showed it Jones & went up & consulted

*Ingram after dinner – on a very snowy night taking Ken
with me.'*

*'Mon March 2nd
1 o'c saw Dr Dudgeon at St Thomas's. He advised me to
see the firm & get them to withdraw Hugh's name.'*

I initially assumed that the stomach powder with Hugh's
name on was medication for him, but the latter entry makes it
clear that this was some kind of patent dispute, and Kenneth
confirms in his memoir that his father was involved in a patent
dispute with Macleans around 1930. He does not suggest
that there was a family connection with the pharmaceutical
company and the similarity of the names seems to have been
coincidental. It was obviously sufficiently worrying for Ida to
go out on a snowy February night to sort it out and to save
Hugh from anxiety. That Kenneth went with her is another
example of the way he was giving her support.

The school Easter holiday found her again trying to divide
herself between Hugh and the children. He was evidently still
unwilling or unable to go away from home, so she shopped,
went to the theatre and ate out with the children, and with
friends, and the children eventually went off for a stay in the
hotel in Minchinhampton on their own, monitored by daily
phone calls. Ominously, Ida started again to record daily
Hugh's sleep patterns, moods and medication, but that was
temporary – in May Hugh really appeared to rally. They
started playing a few holes of golf together – this increased
to full rounds – Hugh started eating more and put on weight,
and Ida seized on the small signs of a return to normality:

'H unpacked his fishing rods'

'Brought me in my coffee after dinner.'

'Played 10 holes of golf with Hugh at Wimbledon Park. H looked at damage to car from a woman running into us yesterday.'

'H had a whiskey & soda at dinner the 1ˢᵗ time for months.'

The family spent most of July and the whole of August in Minchinhampton. Scotland was out of the question, but this was an important milestone since it was the first time in nearly a year that Hugh felt able to leave home. But he was not improving fast enough for the management board at St Thomas's, who, nearly a year after the onset of his illness, were starting to raise the issue of his resigning. At the beginning of July, before they left for Minchinhampton, Ida had a particularly fraught day:

> *'Tues July 7ᵗʰ 1931*
> *9.30 Dr Dudgeon.*
>   *Called at 49 Norfolk Square re new nurse.*
>   *Had a long interview at the Lister with Robison about the action of the Dept. Sci & Ind in reducing their grant. Called on Hugh's bank manager & transferred A&N shares to the Bank agst overdraft till Sept.'*

Dr Dudgeon, professor of pathology at St Thomas's, had come to talk about Hugh's future, and this was followed by a conversation with Robert Robison, Ida's head of department at the Lister, in which, it seems, they discussed the decision of the Department of Science and Industrial Research to reduce their grant. This had been Ida's funding since the end of the war, but it is not clear whether it was her personal funding that was being reduced or funding to a group at the Lister. If it was her personal funding, might this have been connected with the fact that her research output had necessarily diminished in the past year? Her response – perhaps to both interviews – was a visit to the bank manager to negotiate an overdraft by transferring shares as security. This is the first time that she overtly refers to money pressures.

They rented a house in Minchinhampton, taking their housekeeper, Mrs Mowatt, with them. Hugh and Ida were there from 11th July, but Kenneth and Barbara stayed in London to finish the school term – and for Kenneth to take his School Certificate exams (forerunners of 'O' levels and GCSEs). There were nightly phone calls in which he reported on how the papers had gone, but he was expected to be as stoical and independent as his mother was.

Reading the diary, this sounds almost like a normal summer holiday, despite bad weather and dramatic storms. They all went for long walks and played golf; Kenneth hired a bike and went off for long rides; Ida and Barbara went into Stroud for shopping trips. Ida's assertion that *'He is obviously and steadily getting better'* (8th July) seems to be being borne out, until one is floored by the following entry for 14th August:

> *'H very much better today. Discussed Griffiths & signed a testimonial for a post as physiological chemist to the Cancer Hospital which I drew up & read to him.*
>
> *After tea H walked over with me to Minchinhampton to get shaved & came back by bus.'*

Hugh was *'much better'*, but not actually capable of writing a reference for a colleague's job application. Ida wrote the reference and read it to Hugh (did he find even reading a difficult task?). I was interested, too, by the reference here, and elsewhere, to Hugh's going into Minchinhampton to get shaved. Was it a holiday indulgence to enjoy a professional shave? Or had he become used to being shaved by his nurses? Earlier in the year he had difficulty writing, so was his hand not steady enough for shaving? Was he not thought safe to be entrusted with a razor? There may be nothing significant about these shaves, but there is a letter from Ida to her father, written that same day, which, though positive as ever in its tone, still suggests that she was not really as sanguine about Hugh as she wanted to be:

'Dearest Father,

Our letters crossed each other – I think – we are still here & I think we shall probably remain until the middle of September when we shall return to London & then everything will depend on the state of Hugh's health so it's very difficult to make plans...

The children are really enjoying their holiday – they don't mind getting wet & play golf & cycle and walk and are both much better for the change already. If only a spell of fine weather would come.

I do see a really great improvement in Hugh since we have been here. Ken & he play about 8 to 12 holes of golf each evening & Hugh is beginning to take more interest in it & to get less tired. I try to get him to walk including the golf about 3 to 4 miles a day but he still can't do long spells. However I think the next few weeks are going to make a great difference to him. He is certainly sleeping better.

Have you yet fixed on where the annual Roneo meeting is to be held? I expect it is already making you very busy. Are you going to have any holiday yourself and where are you going to spend it? I hope to hear some news of you soon? Have you seen Connie and Max since their return?

> *Very much love my dear father & let me know soon*
> what *is happening to you.*
> *Ever your Di.'*

The tone is affectionate and she asks a lot of questions about
his plans, but she makes no arrangement to go and see him.
On her previous stays in Minchinhampton with the children,
she had always taken a day to drive over to Limpley Stoke to
see her father, but in the two months they all spent there that
summer there is no mention of a single visit. The letter makes
it clear that they had not fallen out, and later in the autumn
she was actively and affectionately involved in his eightieth
birthday celebrations. She mentions phone conversations
with Gertrude, his wife, too. So I could only conclude that she
did not go to see her father because Hugh would not be able
to cope with the outing and she did not feel that it was safe for
her to go herself and leave him alone.

The authorities at St Thomas's were not convinced of his
recovery, either. As soon as the family got back to London in
mid-September, the axe fell:

> *'Sept 21ˢᵗ.*
>
> *3.0 Had an interview with Dr Dudgeon who wants
> Hugh to send in his resignation.*
>
> *H very agitated in the morning about the Dudgeon
> interview – referred to the fact that he had got all the
> money for the laboratories & said it was useless to keep on
> Griffiths.'*

Hugh protested, Ida continued to seize on signs of his
improvement, but on 2ⁿᵈ October he signed his letter of
resignation, and on 4ᵗʰ October Ida posted it. She recorded
the moment rather formally, aware of its significance:

'Posted H's resignation as Professor of Medicine & Senior Physician at Thomas's.'

They were in a new phase. Ida now had to keep the family finances afloat and had somehow to remain positive about the prospect of Hugh's recovery in the face of discouragement and Hugh's own despair.

CHAPTER NINE

REMAINING HOPEFUL

1932–1933

FRUSTRATINGLY, THERE IS NO DIARY FOR 1932. There must have been one; with the exception of this year there is a continuous chain of indexed diaries from 1930 to 1942, and even if Ida was not in the mood to be discursive in 1932, she must have kept an appointments diary at least. Of course, there are many reasons why one diary might have been separated from the others and then lost, but if the loss was not accidental then we should consider the possibility that Ida herself did not want it to survive.

She clearly wrote her diaries for herself – she was not a politician with an eye to publication and she did not use them for self-justification or self-glorification – but she must have known that others might read them after her death. Her diaries at this stage were primarily a reminder of appointments, with added commentary on how those appointments turned out, and anything of interest that she and the rest of the family did in between these fixed points. She was an instinctive collector of data, and keeping a diary fixes events; the recording itself is a kind of reflection on them. From August 1930, Ida, in effect, lost Hugh as a companion. He was unable to take any real interest in the activities of the rest of the family, and she recorded his fleeting moments of interest as exceptional. That meant, I imagine, that from 1930 on there was very little of the 'How was your day?' debriefing that can take the place of a diary record, and writing up her diary may have become more important to her. She was generally so restrained, though, in her diary entries that it is hard to imagine her writing anything so hurtful that she did not want her family to read it after her death. But 1932 is likely to have been her hardest year yet. By the end of that year, Hugh had been ill for nearly two and a half years, with no real prospect of recovery, and the loss of his salary was putting extra pressure on Ida. If there was frustration or despondency in her 1932 diary, it would not be surprising. (I was reminded that the nineteenth-century astronomer Caroline Herschel tore out of her diary the pages in which she had written her feelings about the marriage of her beloved brother, with whom she worked.)

Without the diary, there is some information from other sources. Barbara writes that 1932 was the year when her mother was finally appointed to a full-time salaried post at the Lister Institute. The timing of this appointment may not have been coincidental. Up until then, with Hugh's substantial earnings to support them, she may have been happy to rely on the 'soft' funding of a series of government research grants, as this gave her flexibility and allowed her the time for her multitude of other commitments. Now, though, her grant was being reduced and, anyway, she needed a salary of her own. She may have applied for the post, or one of her senior colleagues – Robert Robison, for example, with whom she had discussed the reduced research grant in July the previous year – may have made representations on her behalf.

The full-time post brought its own pressures: more meetings, some teaching and the obligation to spend more time in the lab. On the surface, this does not look like a very productive year in terms of her research; she published only one paper[23] that year – and that was in the January, so was the result of work done in previous years – and she published no papers in 1933, which might suggest that 1932 had not yielded much to write about, but this is probably too simplistic an interpretation of the publication record – much of her work was collaborative and papers can have a long gestation.

At the end of her 1931 diary, she listed some dates for the following year:

> 'Concerts C. Sargent Feb 8 March 7 April 11
> Sat June 25 Oxford Annual F.U.W.
> July to Aug Edinb. Conference I.F.U.W'

The Sargent concerts at the Courtauld were a regular fixture, and she continued going to them for many years. The BFUW and IFUW dates are expressions of intent, but Ida had not gone away without Hugh since her brief weekend in Minchinhampton with Kenneth in October 1930, and though I could not find out whether she was at the Oxford meeting, I did find clear evidence that she missed the important IFUW conference in Edinburgh. After a fruitless search of the IFUW archive for reference to Ida's presence at the conference, I happened on two letters among the memorabilia; they had been slipped into a folder which otherwise contained family snapshots. Both the letters, dated early in August 1932, regret her absence from the conference. The first, from Winifred Cullis, opens:

---

23 *Biochemical Journal* 'The influence of succinic, fumaric, malic and ace-

'Aug 1ˢᵗ 1932

Dearest Ida,

We have been missing you all the time most dreadfully and thinking of you and wishing you were here. The conference on the whole has gone exceedingly well but it would have gone just a little bit better if we could have had you with us. Dame Margaret of course has been good in a way and at certain points but she cannot be heard and is terribly nervous...'

And after some anecdotes about conference mishaps, she goes on:

'People are continually asking about and regretting your absence...'

The second letter is from Alys Russell (wife of philosopher Bertrand Russell):

'Aug 5ᵗʰ '32

Dear Mrs MacLean,

I cannot tell you how much you were missed at Edinburgh... and how many good wishes there were for your health and happiness. Except for your absence, however, the conference went off perfectly without a hitch of any kind.'

We can see that *'without a hitch'* was hardly Winifred's view, but both letters work hard at conveying how much her absence was felt while reassuring her at the same time that all went well without her guiding hand. For her, missing this

---

tic acids on the deposition of liver-glycogen' by Annie Phyllis Ponsford, Ida Smedley-MacLean, January 01 1932.

milestone conference of the organisation she had worked so long and hard to build must have been a real deprivation, and the fact that she did feel that she could not leave Hugh even to go as far as Edinburgh is powerful evidence of how fragile his mental health still was. I wonder, in fact, whether Hugh may have gone into residential care at some point during this year, but that is speculation based on events in the following year and I shall come to it later.

If she had time and energy to interest herself in the outside world – and she generally did – then she will have found plenty to think about. The year 1932 was a starting point for many of the issues that dominated the decade, and some events are worth recording here because they set the scene for the years to come.

In January, the Archbishop of Canterbury, Cosmo Lang, issued a ruling that divorced people could not remarry in church; this would have a direct effect on the events which led to the constitutional crisis in 1936 and the abdication of Edward VIII.

In May, James Chadwick, working at the Cavendish Laboratory in Cambridge, identified the neutron as an elementary particle present in the atomic nucleus – a discovery that was exploited to create the atomic bombs that were dropped on Hiroshima and Nagasaki and heralded an age of nuclear weapons.

In the German Federal Election in July, the Nazi party became the largest party in the Reichstag for the first time. In January 1933, Adolf Hitler would become Chancellor.

In September the National Hunger March, the largest of the 1930's hunger marches, set off from Glasgow to walk to London.

In October, Sir Oswald Mosley relaunched his 'New Party' as the British Union of Fascists.

In the area of women's achievements, on 23rd April, the new Shakespeare Memorial Theatre was opened in Stratford-upon-Avon by the Prince of Wales. The architect Elizabeth

Scott had been the only woman to enter the international competition to design the new theatre and had defeated more than seventy other entrants to win the commission. She was only thirty – not yet old enough to vote under the terms of the 1918 suffrage bill. The following month, Amelia Earhart flew the first solo crossing of the Atlantic.

What else may have happened in Ida's life during that year is a matter of conjecture, but there is a marked difference in her approach to Hugh's illness at the opening of her 1933 diary; at the end of 1931, she was not reporting on his condition every day but was still noting particularly good or bad days. In January 1933, there are only two mentions of him – on one occasion he met her after work and they walked home, and on the other the children were both out on a Saturday evening (fifteen-year-old Barbara at a school dance in her first evening dress), so *'Hugh and I in alone in the evening'*. This was at the end of January and there are no further references at all to Hugh in February and March, with just one – brief and enigmatic, *'H to Bailey'* – in April. Ida herself was back at work and into her Lyceum and Crosby Hall work with full vigour: twelve Lyceum Club meetings from January to April, four Crosby Hall meetings, seven BFUW meetings (she was still Chair of the BFUW), plus meetings of the Council of the Chemical Society and of the Biochemical Society. She was also regularly at the lab and at work-related meetings and talks, and there is more detail in her diaries than before about the work she was doing – for example:

'Sat 18

Went round with Barbara in the morning & to my bank & the lab. Had a talk with Robison on Zilva's attitude to Szent-Gyorgy's[24] hexuronic acid as vitamin C and Harris's paper at the Biochemical Society.'

---

24 Hungarian biochemist, former student of Gowland Hopkins, credited

and:

> 'Mon 12 Called to Barbara with a bilious attack at 1 am.
> 7.50–8.30 am organic chem with Ken. 10–1 lab. Casimir
> Funk[25] came in, recently discovered that pregnandiol or a
> similar substance from urine increases methyl glyoxal or
> similar aldehyde in urine. Neptune Hall 1.50. Home to
> lunch to see Barbara. Rung up by Miss Johnstone and
> BFUW accountant. Went up and called on Mr Jones,
> met his doctor there & saw Mrs Hall his landlady – then
> came home.'

This second entry is another example of the multitasking days that delighted me as I read them: a broken night looking after her sick daughter, forty minutes of breakfast-time organic chemistry coaching for her son, a morning at the lab, a dash home to check on her daughter, telephone calls about the BFUW, a visit to check on a sick colleague and then, finally, home. (Mr Jones was suffering from acute pneumonia; Ida was concerned that the work he had been doing on phosphoryl chloride in the lab had exacerbated the problem.)

With this picture of a busy life not dominated by concerns over Hugh in my mind, I assumed, when I found the schedule below, covering the second half of April, that Hugh was so much better that Ida felt able to take two weeks to attend the Lyceum International Congress in Rome and to take the opportunity to include an energetic round of sightseeing:

> 'Sat 15 via Newhaven and Dieppe
> Sun 16 Paris 8.05 to Modane

with first isolating vitamin C, winner of the Nobel Prize for Physiology or Medicine in 1937.

25 The Polish biochemist generally credited with identifying the unknown factors which he named 'vital amines' or 'vitamins'.

7.20, Mon 17 Modane to Rome,
Tue 18 – Sat 22 In Rome
Sun 23 To Naples and overnight there
Mon 24 Pompeii
Tue 25 Capri, (Wed 26 return to Rome?)
Thu 27 Return train to Modane and stay overnight
Fri 28 train to Paris (Sat 29 return from Paris to home)'

She certainly did attend the meeting, but not because Hugh was better. Two days after her return from Paris, she wrote:

'MAY
Mon 1
To the lab in the morning and bought garments for Barbara. Ken, Barbara and I drove down to Midhurst & had tea with Hugh & walked in the woods with him. H apparently better.'

There is no indication in the entries before this that there had been any kind of crisis precipitating Hugh's move into residential care, but he was now in a medical facility of some sort, and Ida recorded visiting him, from then on, every Sunday, either alone or with one or both of the children, until October, when he returned home. What had happened? Was the move intended as temporary respite care while Ida was away in Italy? The enigmatic reference in April – 'H to Bailey' – that I referred to above is dated 13th April, just two days before she set off. This, I think, was Hugh's departure to Midhurst (West Sussex), as Dr Bailey is mentioned later as his consultant there. There is none of the detail that she included around Hugh's transfer to the hospital in Penshurst at the beginning of his illness. Perhaps this is because she was distressed – or possibly guilty – about the move, or perhaps it was not a major event because it was part of a plan. This is speculative, but a diary entry in early October recording that she 'talked over Hugh's return home for the winter' with one of the doctors at Midhurst does suggest that there had been an intention for Hugh to spend April to early October in Midhurst – the months when he could benefit most from fresh air and exercise. These had always been Ida's preferred remedy – walks in the parks, rounds of golf and a summer in Minchinhampton being the best she could do from their London home – so she would have been attracted to a treatment regime in a country hospital or clinic. (Her Sunday visits to Hugh often involved picnic lunches in the woods and rounds of golf.) The decision to send Hugh to Midhurst cannot have been an easy one but he was not making real progress at home and Ida may have felt that her own anxiety to see him better was putting more pressure on him.

The doctors at Midhurst were reassuring. Ida's rather weary, 'H apparently better' is followed by:

> 'I saw Dr Bailey who is quite certain that Hugh is _very much_ better – he was laughing & joking about the shows at a forthcoming fete before we left.'

and:

> 'Dr Symonds telephoned to me after seeing H at Midhurst – very delighted at the improvement.'

Ida made the best of the lonely business of taking Kenneth up to start at Cambridge at the beginning of October. The faithful Arthur Field drove them there and Ida was rather delighted when they spotted a wedding party in King's Parade – the marriage of Gowland Hopkins's daughter Jacquetta. She settled Kenneth in digs in St John's Road with 'a nice little landlady who will mend for him', bought him a tea service (tea being an important social ritual at Cambridge) and met Beatrice Thomas for tea before returning home. Proud of him though she was, and hopeful for his future, his going away must have been a wrench for Ida. He had been such a support to her – a companion, escort, chauffeur and listening ear – and he had carried some of the burden of supporting his father, visiting him alone at Midhurst and playing the inevitable rounds of golf.

Barbara, at nearly sixteen, was becoming a companion, though, enjoying shopping expeditions (she and Ida shared a love of clothes) and going to the theatre, to concerts and to some of her meetings with her. And a few days after Kenneth left for Cambridge, Hugh returned home. It was a low-key event, but the later diary entries do suggest that they were companionable together: she recorded him meeting her from work, going shopping with her for a birthday present for her father, going to the pictures (Charles Laughton in the newly released *The Private Life of Henry VIII*) and going to change the library books with her. When Kenneth came home from Cambridge for the weekend, he and Ida took Hugh to see Charles Laughton, in the flesh, reprising his portrayal in Shakespeare's *Henry VIII* at The Old Vic. On one occasion she gave up her ticket to a public meeting on an issue that was a current priority for the BFUW in order to go with Hugh to an appointment with Dr Symonds:

'Tue 14 Married Women's Employment Meeting. Gave my ticket to Dr. Klieneberger. Home to lunch meeting Hugh on embankment. I saw Dr Symonds with Hugh 5 p.m. Went up by bus taking a taxi from Marble Arch. Coming back waited a long time for a 30 & finally took a taxi from Marble Arch home. Hugh's first London taxi and buses since July 1930.'

It was a milestone probably worth missing a meeting for.

Though Hugh's return home seems to have been successful, the domestic arrangements at 2 Elm Park Gardens sound to have been fairly chaotic. She was unable to find a reliable housekeeper and in early November, with Hugh newly returned from Midhurst, she came home from the Lister for lunch to find chaos: the housemaid had thrown a plate at the cook, the police had been involved and there was certainly no lunch. I was rather delighted by Ida's account of this incident, which shows her as her most managing, practical, humane self: she was obliged to dismiss Agnes, the housemaid, but she organised a place in a hostel for her before sending her packing. She then 'interviewed the police' – not the usual way round, but I have no doubt that, in Ida's case, she did just that. She then came home for tea, having had no lunch, and went out again to an agency to engage another housemaid and stopped off at Woolworths to buy a replacement plate before returning to the Lister and then meeting Hugh and accompanying him to an appointment with his psychiatrist. A few days later she replaced the cook!

As ever, she was also concerned about the wider family: she made several visits to Limpley Stoke to see her father; she saw Connie and Max and supported their various artistic ventures; and she kept an eye on her nephew, Oliver, and his sisters, Mary ('Peter'), Pamela and Anne. She took them to the theatre, to concerts and out to dinner, and included them in family activities.

She was enjoying theatre again: she and Barbara saw *The Late Christopher Bean*, a popular new comedy by Emlyn Williams, starring Edith Evans and Cedric Hardwicke; and *Richard of Bordeaux* by Gordon Daviot (a pseudonym of Elizabeth Mackintosh, who also used the name Josephine Tey for her detective stories). The play was a highly romantic picture of Richard II as a devoted husband and champion of his people, trying to maintain peace in his kingdom against the onslaught of the usurping Henry Bolingbroke. Starring John Gielgud and Gwen Ffrangcon-Davies, it was a smash hit, the longest-running play in the West End that year. Audiences loved the modern language spoken by the historical figures, and perhaps, in a world that was increasingly dominated by strong-man dictators – Stalin, Mussolini, Hitler – they were ready to see the unwarlike king as a hero, in contrast to his bullying cousin.

Ida had not yet returned to her pre-1930 social whirl of lunches and dinners with friends, but she kept up with Winifred Cullis and Beatrice Thomas, and in October she had a reunion with the Weizmanns which delighted her:

> 'Mon 17 Dined with the Weizmanns & had a very good evening – recapturing the feeling of old times with them.'

She was still supportive of Weizmann's campaign for a Jewish homeland in Palestine and, with Hitler newly installed as Chancellor in Germany, she was already concerning herself with the situation of the German Jews. On 16th May, she attended a public meeting at the Queen's Hall about 'the expulsion of Jews from Germany'. (Jews were not, in fact, being expelled: their citizenship was revoked and they were banned from government employment; those who were able to were emigrating in large numbers.) Ten days later, Ida raised the issue at a meeting of the BFUW executives. They had received an urgent request for help from the German branch of the IFUW to enable some of their members to leave Germany, and throughout the 1930s and 1940s, the BFUW, starting under Ida's leadership, worked unstintingly to help: wrestling with the Home Office, providing the financial guarantees that the government required, arranging accommodation and English tuition, and finding jobs for well-qualified professional women who found obstacles placed in their way (the General Medical Council was already demanding, in 1933, that the government restrict the number of doctors coming into the country, and the dentists followed suit).

This would be a new chapter in the BFUW's story but, in the meantime, they were concerning themselves with another issue; on 21st January, Ida had convened an emergency meeting of the BFUW Executive with one item only on the agenda:

'To consider the following resolution for transmission to the Council of the University of Liverpool at their meeting of January 24th 1933:-

"That the Executive Committee of the British Federation of University Women affirms its strong conviction that marriage in itself should not constitute a bar to the holding of university posts by women: that, in the best interests of the universities, the efficiency of the individual teacher should be the only consideration when making or renewing appointments. Any discrimination against women on the ground of marriage only must react injuriously on the outlook and prospects of women students: that, for these reasons, this Committee views with grave concern the decision of the Senate and Council of the University of Liverpool that the appointments of women members of staff should terminate on marriage."

There is mention of a further discussion at the end of May, but nothing more after that. It would be a long battle; even the BBC operated a 'marriage bar' (though it was rather flexible and could be ignored when it suited). The practice did not become illegal until the Sex Discrimination Act of 1975 was passed.

Ida kept two letters from this period – both a boost to her confidence and both confirming again the energy and skill that she brought to her work for the BFUW and for the Lyceum clubs. A diary entry for Saturday 4th November records that an all-day sale in aid of the BFUW had raised *'the £500 required'*. This was some sale! £500 was roughly the equivalent of £30,000 today – an enormous amount of money to make in a day at a charity sale, and Ida was the driving force behind it. A letter enclosed in that page reads as follows:

'37 Cholmley Gardens, West Hampstead NW6, 15 Nov 1933

Dear Mrs MacLean,

This comes to add my little word of delight and congratulation on the result of the sale. It surpassed anything I had imagined & is a remarkable tribute to your faith and leadership as well as to all the work you manage to do – how is a complete mystery to me. I felt I must send you this note to express my admiration as I am not good at doing it when I meet you.

Yours most sincerely,

Muriel M Dickson.'

There are no details about the nature of the sale, but Ida had obviously managed to persuade people with money both to donate and purchase very freely.

The second letter is dated 19th October, and refers to Ida's chairing of a meeting of the Central Bureau of the Lyceum clubs:

'Bramblebury, Dunsmore, nr Wendover, Bucks

Dear Mrs MacLean,

I really feel I must send you a line to say how much I

admired the way you acted as Chairman at the C.Bureau meeting. With the two "Bolshies" opposite longing for a chance of getting their knives in & the Dutch member who wasn't quite sure of her English & a little misty about things in general you had many difficulties to contend with & I thought you managed splendidly – got business done & gave S & R little opportunity of doing anything. Good chairmen, men or women, are very rare & I greatly hope that whatever you give up it won't be the Chair of the Central Bureau. I felt wonderfully cheerful after that meeting...'

The issue under discussion at the meeting was the future of the London Lyceum club. Ida was on the Executive of the London club, as well as being the Chairman of the Central Bureau of the International Lyceum Association. While many of the clubs were flourishing (some still continue today), the London club was clearly in difficulties, and a law case was brewing in relation to it. There was a flurry of meetings with shareholders and solicitors during November. Ida was hoping that the club's solicitor, Mr Woodcock, could sort out the legal issues and the financial problems, but at the very end of the year, on 28th December, the blow fell: the receivers had been called in and the building had been sold:

'Thu 28 So ends my association with the Lyceum Club and indeed with the club which started in 1902 & with the Central Bureau of the International Association of which I've been Chairman since mother's death in 1923.'

Although she regretted the passing of an era and the passing of a connection that had been a significant part of her life, it may be that dropping this responsibility was something of a relief.

She certainly did not brood on this outcome in the days that followed. The diary is full of her other activities: arrangements about IFUW fellowships, concerns about state interference in the German FUW, time in the lab reading up about lipins in blood plasma, shopping in Harrods and Hamleys sales and going to see the children in a performance that Kenneth had directed of *Rome Express*, a stage version of the film thriller which had come out the previous year. Her final entry, for 31st December reads:

'*Sun 31 Children go to tea to Ledinghams. Hugh up for lunch – sat talking with me re children after lunch then walked along to post office before tea. Played 100 billiards with Ken and 100 with me – very much better. The old year goes out with promise.*'

CHAPTER TEN

THE MIRACLE EVENT

1934–1935

THE PROMISE OF THE NEW YEAR WAS NOT ILLUSORY: Hugh made steady progress and Ida's relief is present on every page of her 1934 diary, not only through her charting of the symbolic moments of his recovery but in the whirl of activity that she recorded and the sheer verve and vigour with which she recounted it.

'*The miracle event*', as she called it, happened in March:

'*Sat 3 Saw Mrs Phillipps (Ladies Victoria Club) & spent morning at lab. H met us – definitely much better, the miracle event.*'

As miracles go, it is a little underwhelming – Hugh had, after all, come to meet her before in the course of the past four years – but the '*us*', I think, is the important word. It reveals just how isolating Hugh's illness had been; he had not been able to face seeing anyone but his immediate family, so she had not been able to do any entertaining at home, in contrast to the pre-1930 stream of guests she had to lunch, tea and dinner, and Hugh had accompanied her nowhere except on solo shopping expeditions. Slowly, he was becoming integrated back into the social life they had enjoyed: on 14th March, Winifred Cullis, always to be relied on, came to dinner with Ida and Hugh – *'very successful'*, she noted – and on 1st April, she, Hugh and Kenneth drove to Limpley Stoke to have tea with her father – *'Hugh's first visit to him for many years'*. Later that month, she had two young researchers from the Lister to dinner, and a few days after that she invited Dr Betty Heimann, a German Jewish academic who had emigrated to the UK the previous year and, with the help of the BFUW, had secured a research post at the School of Oriental and African Studies.

Normal life was being resumed and, when a crisis came in early May, Hugh was actually able to be the support she needed. A phone call on a Saturday evening to tell her that her father had suffered a heart attack was followed almost immediately by another call to tell her that Kenneth, in Cambridge, was seriously ill with a high fever and had been admitted to a nursing home. Ida phoned Beatrice Thomas in Cambridge to ask her to see Kenneth and report back, drove to Limpley Stoke to make arrangements for her father's care, and then spent most of the following week in Cambridge, where she found Kenneth with a temperature of 104.5. Hugh was *'so helpful and considerate'*. He and Barbara joined Ida in Cambridge at the weekend and, when Kenneth was recovering enough for Ida to return to London the following week, Hugh twice drove up to Cambridge alone to see him. It was an enormous change from his passivity of the past four years. It was in Ida's nature to make herself responsible, but she no longer had to take full responsibility for everything. In September, some of Hugh's family came down from Scotland for an extended visit, Hugh saw his first patient in four years, and when the issue of the Macleans powder resurfaced, Hugh dealt with it himself. In November, Kenneth had a real celebration for his twentieth birthday, in contrast to the muted affairs of the previous years. The family had dinner *'with ice pudding and champagne'* and then were driven by Field, in the new car they had just bought, to see a revue in the West End. *'1ˢᵗ time for 41/2 years Hugh has had his dress clothes on. The evening went off very well.'*

Free from anxiety about Hugh, Ida seems to have found new energy for work. The diary is full of notes on work done, work planned, work discussed. She acquired a small lab of her own adjoining her main lab, persuading the Lister's authorities to knock out a door between the two, and started the work on dietary deficiency of unsaturated fatty acids in rats on which she would publish at the end of her career.[26] She published three papers in the *Biochemical Journal* at the beginning of the year: one on palmitic acid[27] with Margaret Beavan Pearce, with whom she had published previously; one with Annie Ponsford,[28] who features often in the diary for this year and was working on a doctoral thesis in Ida's lab; and one with Rachel McAnally,[29] another research student whom she mentored for several years. Ida was continuing her determined practice of supporting and mentoring young women starting out in her field. Outside the lab, she was still on the executive of the Chemical Society, involved in

---

26 Diary entry 26.01.34: *'1st result of feeding the rats on di-, tetra- and hexa-oxystearic for 1 night. Gain after a long flat period respectively 1, 2 & 3 grams'.*

Annotation by R.B. Freedman: *'Presumably these are metabolised to mono-, di- and tri-unsaturated stearic acid and provide dietary source of unsaturated fatty acid which was missing from previous diet.'*

27 *Biochemical Journal* 'The oxidation of palmitic acid by means of hydrogen dioxide in the presence of a cupric salt' by Ida Smedley-MacLean and Margaret Beavan Pearce, January 1934.

28 *Biochemical Journal* 'The oxidation of the fatty dibasic avids and of laevulic acid by hydrogen dioxide in presence of a cupric salt' by Annie Phyllis Ponsford, Ida Smedley-MacLean, January 1934.

29 *Biochemical Journal* 'Note on the storage of carbohydrate and fat by Saccharomyces Frohberg when incubated in sugar solutions' by Rachel Anne McAnally and Ida Smedley MacLean, January 1934.

manoeuvrings around the appointment of a new president and vice-president, and on the Medical Research Council's Vitamins Committee.

The BFUW was engaging actively with helping the German Federation, which was suffering severe restrictions under the Nazi regime, and with finding work and accommodation for the stream of German-Jewish women academics leaving Germany. Ida was personally involved in helping several of them in the course of that year: the Indologist Betty Heimann, mentioned earlier; a Miss von Oertzen, whose German bank had stopped all payments to her, and for whom Ida found free board and lodging at Crosby Hall; and Emmy Klieneberger, who had started working at the Lister Institute. Klieneberger's obituary records that she was invited to do research at the Lister Institute by the director, Sir John Ledingham, and I like to think that Ida had a hand in obtaining that invitation. Initially, her work was unpaid, but she was later appointed to the staff and proved herself to be an outstanding bacteriologist who did pioneering work on mycoplasma, a genus of bacteria which is naturally resistant to many antibiotics. Ida took her under her wing – 'called for Dr Klieneberger' is a running refrain through the autumn – and she spoke German with her. In fact, she started to take German lessons with another emigrée, Dr Corradi Bauer. Ida could almost certainly understand written German; along with English it was one of the two main languages of scientific communication. I assume that she wanted to improve her conversational German for the sake of more comfortable communication with the refugees she was meeting and caring for.

She was still in demand to speak on women's education and careers, and in March she gave up the Chemistry Society AGM to appear before a Parliamentary committee:

'Wed 21 Planned to go to the Annual Meeting of the ChemSoc in Birmingham but had to give it up. Met Mrs Ormerod at Stewarts (11 a.m.) and went before Committee presided over by Sir Claude Schuster to give evidence re the admission of women to consular & diplomatic service. Mrs Ormerod & Mrs Spedan Lewis accompanied me, the latter giving evidence as to buyers for John Lewis & Co (salaries, travelling, account of money handled) – Mr Lloyd of Lewis & Co also gave evidence for us.'

The evidence of Mrs Spedan Lewis (daughter-in-law of the John Lewis stores' founder) regarding the way the stores' female buyers coped with travel and handling money suggests that women's inability to manage these challenging tasks was one of the reasons offered by the diplomatic service for not appointing women!

One of the chief delights of the 1934 diary is seeing a return of the sparks of humour and flashes of acerbic criticism that are present in the 1920s. The diaries written during Hugh's illness show courage, resilience and grit, but not, understandably, humour, and it seems as though the determination to exclude any negative feeling meant damping down her critical faculty as well. Now, with a new lightness of heart, both humour and criticism were back. She was quite ready to criticise herself: 'Fri 16 Biochemical at Lister. Read my paper on palmitic and took too long over it.' She chided herself, and her hero, Gowland Hopkins, was not immune:

'Tue 23
I went to Sir F.G. Hopkins Lecture at U.C. (4.15 for 5) on Methods of Biochemical Research which was interesting but too long & rather inaudible.'

A veteran of meetings of all kinds, she was quite intolerant of bad organisation and inept participants:

> 'Thu 3
> A very bad evening at the ChemSoc on unicellular chemistry opened by Eyre.'

> 'Thu 13
> Women's Employment Federation dinner. Sat by Dame Margaret Tuke – met Winifred Cullis on arriving... Winifred spoke well, Philip Guedalla amusingly. Sir David Milne Watson (gas lightstoke) mistook the situation & allocated to women the jobs which were too much drudgery for the men to do & Lady Astor finished in appalling taste imitating Winston Churchill & telling her story of his attempt to freeze her out of the House.'

Even John Gielgud's famous performance in *Hamlet* was not perfect:

> 'Sat 22
> We all went to John Geilgud's Hamlet in the evening – very good up to the Play Scene but fell off afterwards. Jessica Tandy a very poor Ophelia.'

Characteristically, she found humour in absurd juxtapositions:

> 'Tue 5
> Back by 9.35 train – Bishop of Bristol & unmannerly dog in carriage.'

> 'Thu 1
> Stayed at home in the morning to work. H came down & talked about his heart till 12 o'c. Ordered hat.'

'Sat 10

All day at my sale – opened by Lady Chatterjee – an Englishwoman, barrister, D.Sc of London and a very charming person… Came home dead tired and found H in very irritable mood owing to an unfortunate excess of pepper in the soup.'

Hugh was much more prone to bad temper since his illness, but it is encouraging to find her secure enough about his mental state to allow herself a moment of mockery.

The sadness of the year was the death of her father in November. There had been several health scares and he was obviously very unwell, but the end was sudden. Hugh (with whom she had had a row at lunch time) brought the news to her at the Lister:

'Thu 15

Met H – bad explosion on way home with me from Lister & thro lunch. Returned to Lister. H came in to my room about 4.45 where we were having tea to tell me a telegram had come to say father had passed away. He was dictating letters to G & just fell back & was dead in a few seconds. I went down by the 6.30 train & arrived at the Cliffe about 9.'

William Smedley had left instructions that she should arrange his funeral. She was neither his wife nor his eldest child nor his only son, but we can assume that she was, in her father's view, the only real grown-up in the family. She rose to the occasion although the situation was difficult. Gertrude *'Gave a great display of grief… and was absolutely horrible'*, but Hugh *'was terribly nice and helpful to me & supported me all day, & Billy was nice too'*. She suffered the familiar regret that there were things she would now never say to her father, but she had the comfort of remembering her last visit to him at the end of September:

'Sun 30
Ken drove me down to Bath & lunched at the Cliffe & spent the afternoon with father who is much weaker & very jaundiced but with whom I had a very nice afternoon and we seemed quite near together again.'

He had been an admirable father to a daughter who wanted to strike out into unknown territory, not just supporting her financially but respecting her achievements and taking a real pride in them. We might well feel that the easy relationship of mutual respect that she had with him explains the ease with which she worked with male colleagues and prospered in a male world.

In 1935, Hugh returned to work seriously. He had lost his post at St Thomas's and could not return to it, but he took new consulting rooms in Harley Street and Ida compiled a card index of all the doctors who had written to Hugh during his illness; together they sent out 150 'change of address' cards giving the new Harley Street address. He was soon seeing patients again, and he also spent some time in Ida's lab at the Lister, doing research on blood sugar, though this was not altogether a success:

'Tues Jan 8th 1935
H spent the afternoon in the lab doing blood meas. – the 1st for 4 ½ years, required much waiting on & complained of everything.'

This return to work and the income coming in seems to have

sent Ida shopping, making up for the comparative austerity of the previous four years. She bought furniture, including a Sheraton bookcase, a new dinner service, linen, and quite a lot of new clothes for herself and Barbara. She and Hugh also started looking for a country cottage with land, where Hugh could shoot at weekends. Rather delightfully, when Ellen Gleditsch, Norway's first female professor and a distinguished radiologist who had worked with Marie Curie, stopped off in London on her way to a conference in Paris, she and Ida seem to have spent most of their time shopping. There is something almost skittish about the diary at times, as though Ida was still feeling the lifting of the weight of Hugh's illness – and, perhaps, of no longer being the president of the BFUW after eight years:

> 'Forgot there was an International Relations Cttee and had my hair washed. Went up to Victoria (Hotel Belgravia) to lunch & turned up at the Executive meeting, to see Miss Melville take her first meeting.'

Work at the lab was serious enough, though. She published five papers jointly with research students in the *Biochemical Journal* that year. Two of these were with Rachel McAnally,[30] whom she was continuing to mentor and, incidentally, to draw into the orbit of the BFUW and Crosby Hall. Another two were with Robert Owen Jones,[31] whom she also included in

30 *Biochemical Journal* 'The synthesis of reserve carbohydrate by yeast' by Rachel Anne McAnally, Ida Smedley-MacLean, August 01 1935; *Biochemical Journal* 'The synthesis of carbohydrate by yeast II' by Rachel Anne McAnally, Ida Smedley-MacLean, September 01 1935.

31 *Biochemical Journal* 'The oxidation of the fatty acids in vitro with especial reference to the oxidation of β-hydroxybutyric acid and acetoacetic acids' by Robert Owen Jones, Ida Smedley-MacLean, July 01 1935; *Biochemical Journal* 'The oxidation of phenyl derivatives of fatty acids with hydrogen peroxide in the presence of copper' by Robert Owen Jones, Ida Smedley-MacLean, 01 August 1935.

social and family events. Her last paper of the year was written with Leslie Nunn,[32] with whom she worked, on fat deficiency in particular, for several years, through to the end of her career.

Early in the year, she was approached by the Dean of the London School of Medicine for Women and asked if she would take on a part-time lectureship – three days a week – in organic chemistry. Typically, she felt sure that she could combine this with her full-time post at the Lister, but Sir John Ledingham had other ideas, and she had to turn the offer down.

Though no longer president of the BFUW, she was still much engaged: in befriending the German women who continued to find their way to the UK and in facing, with the BFUW executive, the issues for the federation of increasingly dangerous European politics. There was, for example, the issue of the Villa Doccia. This was a villa in Fiesole, outside Florence, which had been offered to the BFUW by an American – a Mr Cannon – through a connection with Alys Russell. Fiesole is a charming and interesting town with Etruscan walls and a Roman amphitheatre. In happier times, it would have been a great asset to the BFUW – a place for its members to enjoy study breaks, hold conferences or just relax and recuperate – but Mussolini was at the peak of his power and there was no enthusiasm among BFUW members for taking on the upkeep of a place which none of them might wish – or be able – to visit. With regret, they declined the offer.

At home, the National Government, led by the Conservatives, was returned to power in the general election, and King George V's Silver Jubilee was celebrated with great pomp and fanfare. There was no repetition of the previous year's hunger march, but there would be more in the next two

32 *Biochemical Journal* 'The oxidation products of the unsaturated acids of linseed oil' by Leslie Charles Alfred Nunn, Ida Smedley-MacLean, 01 December 1935.

years. Ida's diary is full of domestic detail, unimportant in itself but a vivid picture of the time and of the social system that would disappear in the conflagration of the coming war.

Finding and replacing servants is a running theme throughout the diaries, but in 1935, the servants' entrance to 2 Elm Park Gardens seems truly to have been a revolving door. I counted three cooks and seven house parlour maids, six of whom quit their posts in short order. They variously complained about their rooms, did not like Chelsea and failed to work out their week's notice, and caused so much 'unpleasantness' below stairs that it had spread up into the rest of the house. Why the MacLeans could not keep their maids is something of a mystery; they seem to have treated the servants well. That Christmas, they invited the staff to join the family party in the afternoon and to listen to the King's speech on the radio. The Christmas presents they were given sound substantial, but the latest parlour maid still packed up and left as soon as she had received her week's wages three days later. Ida did eventually acquire a very good cook who served up an excellent dinner for Kenneth's twenty-first birthday and for Christmas lunch, though even she caused a *'fearful bother'* over some rabbits which Hugh had brought back from a shooting trip:

'Tues Nov 19th 1935
A fearful bother this morning as Gladys had cut up for cooking 6 rabbits. H had meant 2 of them + 2 which were apparently Cyril's for his secretary. The game brought home has never been used before without arranging with me but H completely exonerated Gladys & blamed me for neglect & mismanagement.'

'*Neglect and mismanagement*': a residue of Hugh's illness was ongoing bad temper – with Ida, with the children, even with the results of the general election, but it is possible that he had a point in criticising Ida's household management, borne out by the disappearing parlour maids. Ida was clever, talented, competent, charming and kind, a first choice to chair a difficult meeting or to organise a successful fundraiser, but it may just be that domestic management was her Achilles' heel.

Her struggles with domestic staff offer a snapshot of the time; in the economic depression, domestic work was still the main employment available to women, but the opportunities for other work that the war had offered meant that it was a less attractive option than it had been. The young women who came and went in Elm Park Gardens complaining about their bedrooms, about Chelsea and about the other servants, wanted a wider workplace and they wanted choice. And the MacLeans were not at the top of the social pile; there were smarter, richer, more aristocratic households to work in. Ida and Hugh received Christmas cards from such distinguished people as the Foreign Secretary Sir Samuel Hoare (was he perhaps a patient of Hugh's?), and Ida mixed with titled women in her voluntary work, but the aristocracy had its own mores and exerted its own patronage, and the MacLeans were some way down in the pecking order. Lord Woolavington, a long-time patient of Hugh's, on whose estate in Aberdeenshire Hugh had gone shooting every August, was now seriously ill and summoning Hugh frequently to see him at his home, Northaw House in Herefordshire. In return (aside from the medical fees) the MacLeans received the patronage of gifts through the year from the various Woolavington estates – in January a large case of Yellow and Red Delicious apples from the Woolavington ranch in British Columbia, in April a box of daffodils and in May a box of lilacs. And when Lord Woolavington died in August, he left Hugh £5,000 (more than £300,000 today).

As well as domestic difficulties, there were family problems. Kenneth and Barbara were doing well – Kenneth passed various medical exams and Barbara, at the end of the year, was offered a place at Newnham to study history (Ida having unashamedly 'put in a word' for her on a visit to Cambridge), but there were problems with the rest of the family: Connie was very unwell and now completely blind, but adhered to her belief in Christian Science and refused to go for medical treatment; and Billy's appearances in the diary made me think of nothing so much as a character in a sitcom. He came frequently for meals and to take away pheasants and other luxuries, and in return he gave advice on stocks and shares. Ida reported on the advice without comment, but since Billy himself was making so little money, he was relying on Ida to feed him I wonder how seriously Ida and Hugh took these 'tips'. Ida not only fed him but continued to keep an eye on Olive and on their children, whom she took to concerts and theatre and out to social events. Finally, there was Gertrude. William Smedley had left all his money and property to her, but she haggled over furniture and personal items, bombarding Ida with letters which ranged from 'unpleasant' to 'horrid'. On one occasion, she wrote asking if Ida would write her a reference for a job as a housemaid (the implication being, presumably, that Ida treated her as though she were still a housemaid – and perhaps she did). She seems, by Ida's account, to have become slightly unhinged, carrying a heavy strongbox everywhere with her, containing, she claimed, all the jewels that her husband had bought her. If Billy seems to come from a sitcom, Gertrude belongs in a melodrama.

And life with Hugh, though infinitely better than it had been at its worst, was not as it had been in those golden years of the late 1920s, and never would be again. Ida noted the bursts of bad temper but never complained or judged. She understood what he had suffered during his illness, and was still suffering as a result. There was a poignant moment when she looked round Guy's Hospital, where Kenneth would be completing his medical training, and remembered the elation of Hugh's success in getting new laboratories built at St Thomas's:

'Fri Nov 15th 1935
At the lab 10 to 3.30 – went up to Guys to a Biochemical to see Ken's future hospital; it looked very attractive in the evening light & I like it built round an open space. It brought home to me rather vividly what H has lost.'

CHAPTER ELEVEN

A GREAT MANY FOREIGNERS

1936

THE 1936 DIARY IS QUITE DOMESTIC IN ITS FOCUS and, for the first time, there are suggestions of real tensions between work and home commitments. Ida was nearly sixty and was not juggling the different strands of her life with quite the cheerful ease that she had managed previously. As Hugh returned to normal life, he may not have appreciated how much time she was obliged to give to her work, now that she had a full-time post. In the years before his illness, she had enjoyed the flexibility of having her own funding and setting her own work schedule, and during his illness she had put a great deal on hold in order to spend time with him. Now, the lab demanded her full attention during the week, and she was full of research ideas and plans which found their way into the diary in a way they had not previously. At the same time, Hugh was more demanding, obsessive about time-keeping and still prone to irritability. Ida sometimes worried about this, afraid that it was a warning of returning depression, but she bore it patiently and accepted blame when she thought it was due. '*Complaint about buttons – justified*' she wrote in early February (but she didn't get round to sewing on the buttons until ten days later!) and *'Explosion this morning over a tactless remark of mine about shoes'*. There were the usual problems with servants, especially cooks – *'Mrs Waite has just been in to say we had forgotten it was her afternoon out & Elisabeth refuses to cook the joint ordered for dinner so I agree to do it'* – and Hugh complained about everything from the breakfast coffee to the food served at a dinner party which Ida thought *'a successful evening'*. Hugh's other frustrations were with the car: the faithful Field had retired and had been replaced by Cyril Housden as Hugh's (*'extremely inefficient'*) chauffeur and secretary. Breakdowns in the car are a running theme in this year's diary, with the car declared *'ruined by neglect'* at one of the garages they took it to. Ida *'spoke to'* Cyril and he left soon afterwards!

Life was further complicated by their decision to look for a country *'cottage'* where Hugh could escape and enjoy shooting, which had become his main relaxation. Early in the year, they went on several fruitless expeditions into Gloucestershire and the Cotswolds looking at properties (*'The Bungalow Residence turned out to be an Army Hut'*) but eventually found what they were looking for – Pinnock Warren, in Gloucestershire: *'H K B & I drove down to Pinnock Warren. We all love it & the wood is entrancing & we agreed to purchase it for £1,550. It swarms with rabbits.'* Although the woodland was entrancing, the cottage was not, and they decided to knock it down and rebuild, leading to endless planning meetings and negotiations with builders and workmen. This second home would turn out to be an enormous drain on Ida's time and energy in the years that followed, but she believed it was what Hugh needed.

She was still being harassed by Gertrude over her father's estate, dealing with solicitors' letters which distressed her and *'imputed to me dishonest conduct'*, and, for the first time, she was worried about Kenneth, who she felt was stressed by his approaching finals, especially as a fellow student had hanged himself. She was supporting Connie financially and trying to persuade her to have an operation on her cataracts to try to regain her sight. Billy was also in need of help, and Ida was continuing to 'mother' Oliver and 'Peter', though Oliver was proving himself far more focused than his father and, at the age of twenty-five, was made a partner in the firm of chartered accountants for which he worked. Ida and Hugh helped him to buy into his partnership and it was to Ida that he entrusted the formal letter, kept between the pages of her diary, declaring that Mr W.O. Smedley had been taken into a partnership with Wyatt, Williams and Hickman, Chartered Accountants.

Her other family concern was with Hugh's professional reputation. Although he was now in demand again as a consultant in private practice and was appointed to consultant's posts by the London County Council at Mile End, New End and Highgate Hospitals, his standing in the scientific and medical world had suffered serious damage from his breakdown, coming as it did at the peak of his professional success. Ida was determined to restore his reputation and set herself to get him elected a Fellow of the Royal Society – a significant honour awarded to mark a lifetime of scientific achievement. The following – very charming – letter makes it clear that Ida had been active in putting forward a nomination for Hugh to the Royal Society and that it had failed:

'The Beeches, Ballater, Aberdeenshire. 10 Oct 1936.
Dear Mrs MacLean,
Your confidential letter has been forwarded to me here & I am very glad to have it. I hope I need hardly say that I agree unreservedly & most heartily with every word that you write about your husband's work. It is just

what I have been saying – more emphatically – for many years. I feel very strongly that he ought to have had the fellowship a while ago; it was indeed disappointing that the nomination was not successful. The thing to be considered now is how & when to raise the matter again. We shall be returning home next week & I shall look up the R.S. Yearbook & see who are on the Council of the Physiology Committee at present, & I will communicate with some friends to ascertain how the land lies & what would be the wisest course to follow. It is delightful to hear that your husband is so well & enjoying his work – after all that you have both passed through in those terrible years. The news of his recovery was the happiest news that we had got for many a year – in times when many friends were falling away & disasters were many. You were splendidly brave & optimistic through it all & it is good to think that you have been rewarded.

I wonder whether he will be able to write & publish something ere long, to let the medical world know that he is really back in health & vigour... That might be important in view of a nomination. I will write to you as soon as I get anything definite.

With kindest regards, yours very sincerely,
E. MacWilliam.'

This was one endeavour in which Ida failed. The advice from Dr MacWilliam that Hugh needed to publish something that would assure the medical world that he was 'really back in full health and vigour' was not taken up, and Hugh was never elected an FRS.

Despite all the distractions, her work is an unbroken thread running through the diary, with more detail about her ideas and plans appearing than ever before; it seems almost that she forgot at times that the diary was not her lab notebook. So, for example, on 29th May, she reported on a lecture she attended at the Chemical Society, given by her old friend Robert Robinson, on biochemical synthesis. She was very excited by the implications of what he had to say for her work on yeast and she recorded the resulting ideas in detail, pleased that they *fitted exactly with our yeast work*.

She was working on yeast carbohydrate with Rachel McAnally, and on fat deficiency with Leslie Nunn. '*Only palmitic hangs fire*', she wrote in January, but it is clear later that she herself was doing the lab work on that. She was doing a great deal of writing, and not just for the *Biochemical Journal*. In January she sent off an article that had been commissioned for a German publication, *Enzym Forschung* (she had flu and sent Cyril, the chauffeur, to fetch the typescript from the Lister so that she could work on it in bed). In May, she was asked by Dorothy Needham, a Cambridge protegée of Gowland Hopkins, to contribute an article to a book which Cambridge University Press planned to publish to mark Gowland Hopkins's seventy-fifth birthday. Later in the year, she was simultaneously writing an article on cholesterol and a paper on unstable yeast carbohydrate. She liked to write at home, where she was free from interruption, but there is a suggestion that Hugh resented this:

> '*I came home at lunch time and worked at the paper with Rachel McAnally on yeast carbohydrate. H rather irritable with me.*'

She obviously enjoyed working with Rachel McAnally, but she knew that it was time for her to move to a full-time post and independent research. In the course of the year, she wrote several testimonials for her and tried to get BFUW research funding for her, and eventually, in November, the job offer came:

> 'Miss McAnally is leaving me next week as Kings have offered her a full time job.'

The entry has a formal tone here, as often happened when she felt she was writing something significant – Rachel became 'Miss McAnally' – but 'is leaving me' reveals how personally she felt her departure and, in fact, they continued to collaborate in their work after McAnally's move to King's.

She had also tried to find a post for Leslie Nunn, but in the end he stayed with her at the Lister (although she did have to speak to him at one point about inappropriate 'sentimental passages' in the laboratory with a Miss Muggeridge!) and did not leave until the outbreak of war.

She was as active as ever in going to Chemical Society and Biochemical Society meetings to hear others speak about their work, though she was a keen critic of presentation. She admired good presentation in others but was also intolerant of a poor performance. So, Lord Rutherford got a glowing review:

> 'Wed Feb 12th 1936
> Went to hear Lord Rutherford give the Faraday lecture – on Radioactivity & the Atomic Theory. Very excellent… such keenness & enthusiasm. It was all so clear & simple.
> Gave my extra ticket to L. Nunn who was very thrilled & impressed.'

She was merciless, however, about three hapless young men giving papers at a Burlington House meeting, who seem to have managed to commit between them all the cardinal sins of bad presentation:

'Spent the morning at Burlington House at a discussion on surface phenomena of membranes. Rideal & Adams very good but the 3 young men who followed, Gee, Askew & Mitchell gave their papers execrably – Gee in exhaustive detail, Askew entering turning his back on his audience & lecturing to his slides & Mitchell gabbling & unable to let go for a moment of his written sheets. All called to order for being too long.'

Even her friends in the IFUW were not immune from judgement. At the IFUW conference later in the year, she noted:

'Dined at the Francuski & in the evening went to the 1st members meeting where Karin Koch read an excellent & everybody else extraordinarily bad papers.'

Her critical judgement could be more general, too: at a rather dazzling social gathering – a Women's At Home at Lady Astor's – she was pleased to meet General Evangeline Booth of the Salvation Army and the distinguished painter Dame Laura Knight, but was less thrilled to be reunited with an old colleague from her days in Manchester: 'I met & talked with Marie Stopes, not improved by age'.

Finding academic posts for the BFUW's German refugees was still a major concern. Emmy Klieneberger had progressed from 'voluntary' work at the Lister to a paid lectureship, but Betty Heimann was still, it was generally acknowledged, being exploited at the School of Oriental Studies. At the beginning of 1936, Ida committed herself to hustling the School's director, Sir Philip Hartog, to find funding for a proper post for Heimann, but without success – the following diary entries suggest that Sir Philip's indolence and indifference to

Heimann's situation were more than a match both for Ida's charm and for her persistence:

'Sat Jan 4th
Rang up Sir Philip Hartog 3 times today and eventually got on to him to talk about Betty Heimann's future. He says that there is no doubt as to the outstanding nature of her scholarship and that if it weren't for the deficit they are faced with, the School of Oriental Studies would make a lectureship for her. ...I think he probably wants a little stimulating to do more. I told him we felt there ought to be some more permanent post than scholarships or Fellowships for her.'

'Fri Jan 24th
Heard from Sir Philip Hartog that we may send our subscr. to the fund for Betty Heimann to the School of Oriental Studies. He feels forming a cttee to raise the money would involve too much work for him! So Dr Heimann's prospects of a lectureship don't look too rosy.'

They were not rosy. Heimann was actually subsisting on a living allowance from the Academic Assistance Council,[33] set up in 1933 to help German refugees, but the Council regarded the inaction at SOAS as so outrageous that they had stopped her allowance in an attempt to exert pressure. When this failed, Ida gave up hopes of action from Hartog and focused on fundraising instead. Enough money was raised to fund a half-time post for Betty Heimann (described, gracefully, in her obituary as 'created specifically for her'). Eventually, after the war and after Ida's death, she was appointed to a senior lectureship.

---

33 The Council still exists today, as The Council for At-Risk Academics.

The BFUW was doing everything possible to maintain its international links in the face of increasing difficulties in Europe. Ida wrote about a meeting at Crosby Hall, where she was clearly delighted by the international gathering:

'We went to Crosby Hall where I took the Chair at an informal party. Dr Melville spoke of the early days of the women's movement. A full room & a great many foreigners – Campanor from Spain, Kuranda (Austria), Hamburger von Oetzen Heimann Klieneberger Rosenau Rupp (Austria), France Hungary Norway & America, many others represented.'

It is at this point that her diary started to include the news from the outside world which had been present as a backdrop until then but now took centre stage. In early March, there are a number of entries about the news from Germany:

'The exciting political news today is that Hitler has marched an army into the demilitarised zone & made a most reasonable speech offering to come back into the L of N & to make nonaggression pacts with his neighbours.'

'Listened to the wireless – an observer from Paris reported that feeling in France is no negotiations until troops are evacuated from the Rhineland. The Locarno signatories are to meet in London on Thursday & the League Council to meet here at the end of the week.'

'Professor Morley lent me a copy of The Week in which it is stated that in the event of serious pressure on Germany (apparently if the Eden group win against the Baldwin *group) the possibility exists of (a) an immediate Nazi rising in Northern Czechoslovakia, (b) acceleration of the attack on Austria, (c) the slim chance of a Ruckswehr-Schacht putsch to eliminate the Nazi wildness & extricate the army from the possibility of a war for which it is "not quite ready".*

In her late thirties, at the outbreak of World War I, Ida was only just in the generation that lost so many, but her husband and her brother both served in the armed forces and now her son was of the age to be called up if there was another war. We can read in these entries the desperate hope that another war could be avoided: Hitler's *'most reasonable'* speech, the planned meeting of the League of Nations, the possibility of a putsch in Germany *'to eliminate the Nazi wildness'*.

In August, the IFUW felt confident enough about the situation in Europe to hold its conference in Cracow, but it was perhaps an indication of the level of tension that one of the British members was stopped and arrested at the border:

'Tuesday, Aug. 26ᵗʰ
The Council meetings have gone off very well, but the pleasure of the meeting has been considerably damped by the arrest of Mrs Atkinson who was detained 24 hrs, 24 hrs in prison & 24 at Warsaw for not declaring a letter of credit & so far it has been impossible to get her release. Today is the opening. meeting'

Mrs Atkinson was released eventually and arrived at the conference amid much rejoicing. Ida, meanwhile, went to a bank to check that her credit arrangements were in order. One is reminded again of how indefatigable these women were.

Inserted in these pages are seven small visiting cards which Ida was given in the course of the meeting, which demonstrate vividly the international and social reach of the IFUW. They came from Dinah Abragam (working at a medical research institute in Paris), Kazimiera Illakowicz (at the Foreign Office, Warsaw), Stanislawa Goryniska (a journalist from Cracow), Marian Whitney (Professor Emeritus of Vassar College, USA), Dr Spur Endrene (from Budapest, President of Hungarian Soroptimists), Princess Leonie Lubomirska (Poland) and a Miss Ackermann (a histologist at Cracow University). The group photograph seems to mark the end of an era. There would be one more conference in Stockholm in 1939, before the world descended into chaos and there would be no more such meetings.

At the end of the year, UK politics dominate the diary – the abdication crisis engaged Ida as it did everyone else. Earlier in the year, she reported at length on the public reaction to the death of King George V, concluding that:

'I really don't think there is anywhere anything but sincere respect & affection for the late king as a man who did his duty and kept before him a very high ideal of it – and during all these years on the throne or at any rate since the war no breath of scandal seems to have touched him.'

She was less certain about the new King Edward VIII, commenting that the Prime Minister's words about the new king:

'somehow left me with the impression that he hoped Edward would be a good King but didn't feel too sure about it.'

The next day, she added:

'H has heard various stories of his past which we hope he'll now keep clear from. Everyone agrees he has brains & sympathy & understanding.'

Everyone was due to be disappointed, of course.

From early December onwards, Ida was reporting daily on the issue of Mrs Simpson, to the exclusion of everything else: the gossip, rumours, parliamentary debates and furious discussions at tea parties, over dinner, at the lab, and in committee meetings.

Ida knew where she stood; nothing if not stringent, she had no sympathy for a king who put his 'personal inclinations' before his duty. She recorded the abdication as follows:

'Fri Dec 11th 1936
8.30 p.m. We are to hear Edward Windsor at 10 p.m. tonight make his farewell speech to his people & give

allegiance to his brother. His abdication took effect at 1.52
p.m. today when he gave the royal assent. The uncertainty
of the last week has disappeared & there's a general feeling
of relief and a feeling that it's much the best solution –
and that Edward has let his country & Empire down, by
putting his own inclinations before his obligations. It is
said that he thought his personal popularity was so great
that he thought the nation would have agreed to Mrs
Simpson & that he has been very badly advised by his
personal friends. Now the papers are full of pictures of the
new King & Queen & their domestic life.'

The newspapers made much of the happy family life of the
new king and queen and the pretty little princesses. Ida knew
as well as anyone the strength that came from that domestic
happiness; she had fought heroically to hold her family
together through the years of lonely uncertainty and knew the
value of it if anyone did. She ended the year, as she so often
did, on a determinedly upbeat note:

'The Duchess of Kent had a daughter born today. The
new King seems to be reigning peacefully & interest in the
Duke of Windsor quite abated & all has settled down.
Sent out about 100 invitations for a sherry party on Jan
7th.'

CHAPTER TWELVE

WAR HANGING OVER US

1937–1939

In 1937 and 1938, the MacLeans, like most people, one imagines, lived a sort of double life; they never lost the consciousness of impending war but at the same time they committed themselves to the urgent demands of everyday life. Diary entries over a weekend at the beginning of September 1938 illustrate this doublethink perfectly:

> 'Sep 10
> Joan and Terry for lunch, tea and dinner. 5 of us to see Noel Coward's "Operette" at Golders Green Hippodrome at night. The children played tennis in the afternoon. A very crisis weekend waiting for the result of the Czech & Sudeten-German negotiations & Hitler's Nuremberg speech on Monday.'

> 'Sun 11
> We all played Monopoly in the afternoon & the children played tennis after tea. A very pleasant weekend.'

A weekend could be both 'very crisis' and 'very pleasant', it seems, though two days later she wrote, 'War hanging over us.'

Work was also filling her days and occupying her thoughts. She published the work, done with Rachel McAnally, on the synthesis of reserve carbohydrate by yeast, in January 1937,[34] and followed that up with a second paper on the subject in September 1938.[35] Now that McAnally had a lectureship at King's College the yeast work was being carried on by Leslie Macleod, who was *rather tiresome in not writing up his work*. (Leslie Macleod went on to a successful career, however, working at the Burden Neurological Institute in Bristol, and specialising in the biochemistry of alcohol addiction.) What was mainly engaging her in the lab was the new work on fat-deficiency disease and on cholesterol. She published two papers on this in December 1938, one with Leslie Nunn[36] and one with Nunn, Margaret Hume and Hannah Henderson-Smith,[37] with whom she had first published in the 1920s. She now had quite a large research team and was finding it necessary to work on the papers at home at the weekends since there were *too many interruptions* at the lab. She could only do this when she was in London, however; weekends at Pinnock Warren required full-time domesticity. They had no servants there, though they did take their cook with them on occasions when they had guests. Ida's accounts of these weekends focus on making up beds, shopping, cooking, washing up and cleaning. She enjoyed them – *a very pleasant weekend* is a frequent comment – and she liked to see Hugh

34 *Biochemical Journal* 'The synthesis of reserve carbohydrate by yeast' by Rachel Anne McAnally, Ida Smedley-MacLean, January 01 1937.
35 *Biochemical Journal* 'The carbohydrate and fat metabolism of yeast' by Leslie Dundonald Macleod, Ida Smedley-MacLean, September 01 1938.
36 *Biochemical Journal* 'The nature of the fatty acids stored by the liver in the fat-deficiency disease of rats' by Leslie Charles Alfred Nunn, Ida Smedley-MacLean, December 01 1938.
37 *Biochemical Journal* 'Studies of the essential unsaturated fatty acids in relation to the fat-deficiency disease of rats' by Eleanor Margaret Hume, Leslie Charles Alfred Nunn, Ida Smedley-MacLean, Hannah Henderson-Smith, December 01 1938.

happy, but it was hard work and she was suffering increasingly from severe sciatica. This was so bad in August 1937 that she did not go up to Scotland with the rest of the family but stayed in London. She was actually quite glad of time on her own: on an occasion in January 1938 she did not go to Pinnock for the weekend with Kenneth and Hugh because she and Macleod were giving a paper at the Lister on the Friday evening. She spent Saturday in the lab and then came home and *Did nothing but read* – "The Warden" [by Anthony Trollope, one of her favourite authors].' *'Very peaceful and a short interval from criticism is a relief.'* Life with Hugh was not easy – his concern with punctuality was wearing, and now that she had two houses to run there was more scope for complaint about her household management. And she was becoming more forgetful. She was not losing her memory, but she was less able to manage the juggling of the different parts of her life and appointments got lost:

'So busy I forgot I had arranged a driving lesson.'

'Rose at 5.30 [after a weekend at Pinnock] *left at 6.30 & breakfasted in London at 9. Lab in morning. We forgot to go to lunch with the Manleys at Wimbledon Park.'*

'Very busy at lab. Forgot a Sale Cttee specially arranged for me at 5.30.'

None of this is surprising: it was an impossibly busy life and she was over sixty.

She did not think of slowing down. She attended innumerable meetings of the BFUW and IFUW, plus residential meetings in Manchester in June and in Paris in July; she was more assiduous than ever in attending meetings of the learned societies – the Biochemical and Chemical Societies, the Royal Institution, the Royal Society, the British Association. She particularly enjoyed meeting the new generation of women and spotting promising newcomers; at dinner after a meeting of the Chemical Society, she met *a very nice girl Miss Crowfoot working on X-ray crystallography of protein at Oxford & who has published with Bernal and got the 1st crystal measurements of insulin*. The nice girl, Dorothy Crowfoot, would become Dorothy Hodgkin OM, FRS, awarded the Nobel prize for Chemistry in 1964 for her work on X-ray crystallography.

She loved keeping in touch with former colleagues, too, and meeting people from across the whole range of scientific disciplines. She and Hugh were invited guests at the funeral, in Westminster Abbey, of Ernest Rutherford, the father of nuclear physics – a sure indication of their place in the scientific world – and an invitation (to her alone) to a reception to celebrate the award of the Nobel Peace Prize to Viscount Cecil for his work for the League of Nations marked her place in the wider political world. Ida and Hugh were moving in interesting social circles in general: Ida had become friendly with the wife of the distinguished archaeologist Max Mallowan – Mrs Mallowan was better known as Agatha Christie – and when they were at Pinnock they were often invited to dinner by the Bowes-Lyons, cousins of the Queen and patients of Hugh's.

She kept up as usual with her old friends and she continued to enjoy a round of lunches and dinners with friends and BFUW colleagues. Her passion for concerts, films and the theatre was undiminished. She went devotedly to the Courtauld Sargent concerts which had been her lifeline under the constraints of Hugh's illness, often taking Oliver or 'Peter' with her, or Barbara when she was home from Cambridge, and she liked to take the younger generation to the theatre too. After being laid low with sciatica in the summer of 1937, she was well enough to see John Gielgud play Richard II at the Queen's Theatre. He directed the play himself and the cast included all the stars of his generation – Michael Redgrave, Alec Guinness and Peggy Ashcroft among them.

Kenneth was still living at home while he finished his medical studies at Guy's Hospital; Barbara wrote to her mother often from Cambridge, and missed her. Both the children were now in serious relationships – Kenneth with Joan Hardaker, whom he had met at Guy's, and Barbara with Hugh Beech, a fellow student who managed and played the drums in a student jazz band. Ida and Hugh must have been a daunting pair to the two newcomers, but Ida was obviously fond of Joan and welcomed her in; she was rather more reserved about Hugh Beech.

As for the rest of the family, Billy had disappeared completely from his wife's and his children's lives – Olive could reach him only through Ida, with whom he kept a tenuous contact. On Christmas Day 1937, he turned up at Elm Park Gardens for supper, looking so ill that Kenneth took him to Guy's and had him admitted. Ida kept a scrawled note from him, thanking them for looking after him. His children were doing well on their own, however: 'Peter' had graduated from Oxford and was enjoying teaching, and when Pamela got engaged to Greville Wellesley Spencer in 1938, Oliver hosted the engagement party. Ida helped Olive to organise (and perhaps pay for) the wedding in October, Kenneth was best man, and Hugh gave the bride away and proposed the toast to the couple.

Billy was excluded, or had excluded himself, but Ida did not let him go; on Christmas Day that year, Billy came for supper ('*soup, cold turkey, pheasant w sausage & ham &*

Ida and Hugh at Pamela's wedding

chip potatoes w trifle lemon sweet & mince pies'), along with
Olive, 'Peter', Pam and Greville, Connie and Max, and the
German refugees Emmy and Hans Klieneberger. They played
tongue-twisters (rather hard on the Germans) and charades:
'*Altogether a very pleasant evening.*' Her entry for the next day
is one word: '*Recovered*'.

Connie's health was a real concern at this time, as were
her and Max's finances. Ida managed to persuade her, finally,
to have an operation on her cataracts, for which Ida paid, but
Connie could no longer make money through her writing;
and though Max was respected as an artist and had a picture
in the Royal Academy Exhibition in 1938, there were several
requests and thank you letters from him to Ida for money sent
during that year.

In September 1938, the prospect of war was starting to fill the diary: Kenneth reported that preparations for up to 30,000 casualties were being made at Guy's and the other London hospitals, and patients who could be discharged were being sent home; Sir John Ledingham told her that he expected the Lister's staff to be evacuated if war broke out and all solvents in the labs were ordered to be removed; Ida's cook, Iris, was urgently summoned home to Wales by her mother, in fear of air raids; friends of Ida's postponed their daughter's wedding because of the crisis and the start of term at Cambridge for Barbara was also postponed.

With the Munich agreement – '*Chamberlain accedes to all Hitler's requests and thus makes peace*' – at the end of September, normal life returned after a fashion: Pamela's wedding went ahead in October, Connie had a cataract removed at St Thomas's, Ida acquired a new cook, Kenneth passed his final conjoint medical exam, and Ida sent off two papers to the *Biochemical Journal* as well as finishing her paper on fat-deficiency disease with Margaret Hume and having a '*general clear-out*' at the lab. She and Joan went for a week's holiday together in Hastings (a real sign of favour from a prospective mother-in-law) and Ida returned to read her paper on fat-deficiency at a Biochemical Society meeting – '*It appeared to be very much approved*' – and organise another BFUW fundraising sale. In November, Ida and Hugh gave a '*very successful*' sherry party to celebrate Barbara's twenty-first birthday (sherry parties were clearly the rage – Ida seems to have floated on a tide of sherry during 1938) and the year ended with her heroic success in gathering the whole family together for Christmas Day supper. Tucked in the back of her diary, dated 31st December 1938, is a handwritten letter of thanks from Lord Baldwin of Bewdley (ex-prime minister Stanley Baldwin) thanking her for her generous donation to the Lord Baldwin Fund for Refugees.

The false calm that followed the Munich agreement meant that war receded in the early months of her 1939 diary (Iris even returned from Wales), and there was a good deal else to concern her. Ill health was a theme for those months. First there was her own: there are quite frequent, but non-specific, mentions of feeling *'bad'* or *'seedy'*, but she does not seem to have consulted a doctor and she was rarely deflected from business as usual. In early January, for example, she had *'a sort of angina attack and a furious headache'* at the lab, but still met Barbara for lunch and went shopping for clothes for her and for ice plates needed for the soirée she was planning in two days' time. She came home with a high temperature and Hugh examined her, diagnosed *'nerve toxaemia'* and sent her to bed, where she stayed for a day, sending Barbara out to order food for the party, but defied Hugh the next morning and spent the day in preparations. The last of the party guests stayed until 2am, but Ida was up early in the morning and at the Lister to examine Leslie Nunn on his PhD thesis. Dr Herbert Raper, the external examiner from Leeds University, was *'quite impressed'* with the thesis; Nunn was granted his PhD and Ida took Dr Raper home for lunch.

The rest of the family came to Elm Park Gardens for nursing: Barbara, in her final year at Cambridge, with her final exams looming, came home with a bad case of flu; Kenneth, now fully qualified – *'now LRCP, MRCC & a real doctor'* was sent home from Guy's with severe tonsillitis; and Hugh's sister, another Barbara (known as Babs), came down from Inverness to have a gallbladder operation at St Thomas's. She arrived looking *'very white and chalky'* and needing to be *'nursed up'* before the operation. Unusually, but not surprisingly, Ida took two weeks leave from work, *'as everything seems on top of me'*.

'I feel completely tired out', she wrote a few days later. *'What with political crises and illness in the house, life is not peaceful'*.

This was something of an understatement, but there was worse to come. Babs had her operation on 3rd April and all seemed to go well, but a week later she developed complications, and in spite of reassurances at the hospital, Hugh was *alarmed and alarming*. He was right; a week later, Babs died, and Ida and Hugh went up to Inverness by train, with the coffin, for her funeral. Babs had been the matron of the Royal Nursing Home in Aberdeen, and was well known and respected in the city. Ida kept a cutting from the *Inverness Courier* which speaks of *'the affection and admiration of her numerous patients'* and quotes the view from her home town of Strathearn that, *'she combined in her personality and character all that was lovely in Highland womanhood'*. Hugh was, of course, deeply distressed, and Ida watched him anxiously in the coming weeks for signs of returning depression.

The refugees were still coming. Ida took in a Dr Jahn from Germany, who moved into Barbara's room when she went back to Cambridge, and a Hungarian refugee whom she settled with the Ryans, their new chauffeur and his wife, who had taken on their mews flat. She was also supporting another refugee, Dr Vera David, a Czech biochemist who went on to a very successful career in the US.

The 1939 diary is full of wedding invitations and photographs; her friends' children were marrying, hurried on, no doubt, by the prospect of war. In June, Kenneth and Joan became engaged, with a wedding planned for early December. Ida was delighted, Joan's mother came down from Bradford to discuss wedding arrangements and domestic concerns dominated once again.

There are frequent letters to Ida from Barbara during this period, happily oblivious of war, preoccupied, as only a twenty-one-year-old can be, with her life, with parties, clothes, riding (which she had taken up under Arthur Field's instruction in London, and continued in Cambridge), exams and what she was to do next. Her boyfriend, Hugh Beech, had graduated and was working for the electronics firm Marconi in Chelmsford, coming to Cambridge at weekends. Barbara's letters suggest that she was still very dependent on her mother, anxious for approval, reassurance and advice. It is clear, though, that she had the family good looks and charm and was a social success in Cambridge; she wrote to Ida that the *Varsity*, the university newspaper, had named her as one of the Cambridge celebrities. Academically, she was less successful; there are two communications to Ida about her final exams, one a postcard reading:

> *'The papers have been absolutely impossible & I have done them even worse than I need have done...'*

and the other a letter:

> *'Dearest Mummy,*
> *...The exam was just awful... Still it is all over now, thank goodness, so I am not doing anything except lie in the sun... dinner with the Boat Club...'*

Though her tutors had thought she might get a 2.1, she ended up with a third. The family were supportive about it; Kenneth's comment was that *'exams are really about as lucky as dog-racing'*, but he had never failed an exam in his life, and in a family of academic high-flyers, the failure must have been hard for Barbara to bear. Later she blamed her mother for persuading her to study economics when she had intended to study history. She *'did not understand maths'*, she said. We can only guess at Ida's reasons for steering her to economics; she may have felt that it would lead to better career prospects, or her feminism may have been a factor – a wish to see her daughter take on a subject thought of as a male preserve. Barbara was immensely proud of her mother – in a letter to her while she was at an IFUW conference in August, she wrote:

> 'You sound a bit depressed about the conference but I'm sure you are doing very well because people are always telling me how good you are and... what a nice woman my mother is!'

But it cannot have been easy to try to live up to her mother's example.

The IFUW conference took place in Stockholm. Ida made the most of the trip, starting out a week before the conference and making slow progress, with Winifred Cullis, up from Gothenburg to Stockholm, enjoying the Swedish countryside, staying in log cabins, going to the coast, taking boat trips and appreciating the food. She then spent a further week in Stockholm and stopped off in Copenhagen on the way home. She must have known that this would be her last trip to Europe for some time; she could not know that it would be her last trip ever.

While she was away, letters swirled between her and the family. Hugh and Barbara were together at Elm Park Gardens, and theirs was not an easy relationship. Hugh's irritability was often directed at Barbara in her teenage years, and she seems to have provoked him at times (challenging the greatness of Robert Burns, for example, and creating 'a tremendous row'!). The situation was made more delicate by the fact that Barbara, still smarting from her exam results, was now taking exams for entry to the Civil Service. Once these were over, she set off for a holiday in Cornwall with friends, and Hugh departed for Scotland, anxious to be there for the Glorious Twelfth. Letters from them mostly ignored the looming crisis, but Ida returned to London to find Ryan, the chauffeur, in uniform, ready for mobilisation, and by 25th August even Barbara requested, '*If anything happens could you please put some cash in my bank?*' Ida went to Pinnock for the weekend and had a phone call from Kenneth, in London, telling her that everyone was leaving the capital and she should stay there. She phoned her head of department at the Lister, Robert Robison, who told her that the director and most of the Lister's staff had sailed for America the previous week. Ida made arrangements to take in evacuees at Pinnock and then returned to London to pack up her lab, see Kenneth and Joan, and close up her house.

Returning to Pinnock, she felt much happier once Barbara arrived from Cornwall. Hugh was still in Scotland and still in denial – '*I do hope that things will blow over once again*' – but on 1st September, as Hitler invaded Poland, Hugh arrived at Pinnock at 1am, having driven all the way as the railways were closed for evacuation. He had stopped in London to see Kenneth, who was busy with the evacuation of Guy's.

Like everyone else, at 11.15 on 3rd September, Ida heard Neville Chamberlain's announcement on the radio that '*this country is at war with Germany*' and they appeared to be settled into life at Pinnock. Hugh fretted about repairs to the car and played golf; Ida sewed blackout curtains, and she and Iris made jam and bottled fruit from their enormous plum harvest. However, by 1st October they were back in London. Ida wrote nothing about their decision to return, or whether the stay at Pinnock was always intended to be temporary, but the London life was picked up again: Barbara was offered a job in the Civil Service working at the Patents Office, Kenneth and Joan came for Sunday lunch, 'Old Nannie' came back to do the cooking, and Hugh went on shooting and playing golf. In the middle of October, Joan's mother, Ethel Hardaker, came for a discussion of wedding plans and Oliver Smedley, a sergeant in the paratroops, arrived on unexpected thirty hours leave and was given half a cold pheasant and a bed for the night.

Work continued – '*Spent day at lab as usual*' – and Leslie Nunn was still working with Ida, though the Lister's staff was seriously depleted. Wedding arrangements occupied November, Kenneth was accepted for a commission in the Navy, Pamela had a baby son and Billy, still a sitcom character, turned up out of the blue with an 'infallible' betting system that would make his fortune before war really broke out!

On 2nd December, Kenneth and Joan were married. It was a church wedding, unlike Ida and Hugh's, followed by a reception at 96 Cheyne Walk, a handsome building near Crosby Hall which now belonged to the Royal Historical Society, but had been the home of the painter James Whistler, and was still decorated with murals by him. Ida entertained family and friends to supper at home afterwards, and they went to see *The Lion Has Wings*, an early propaganda war film, designed to prepare people for war.

On the last weekend before Christmas, Hugh Beech came for the weekend, Ida encountered the Queen and the princesses Elizabeth and Margaret buying cheese in Harrod's, Kenneth was called to report to Chatham, and Barbara informed her father that she and Hugh Beech intended to get engaged.'*H very much opposed, B v unhappy & everything very unpleasant*'. Barbara was angry with Ida, too, for not taking her side, and in later life, when talking to Kenneth's children, she chiefly blamed Ida for discouraging the engagement. Ida described in her diary a tense Christmas Eve, with Hugh Beech making frequent phone calls and Barbara refusing to eat and threatening to leave. Eventually, with some peace-making from Joan and Kenneth, Barbara agreed not to get engaged until Hugh Beech had decided what he intended to do during the war (working for an electronics firm put him in a reserved occupation, doing work useful to the war effort, and he could claim exemption from conscription). Christmas Day supper was not the glorious family event of the previous year, but Oliver and Billy both came, and Ida was grateful enough that they 'all sat down at peace'.

CHAPTER THIRTEEN

ALL THE LOSS AND BRAVERY

1940–1942

'Sleep after toil, Port after Stormy Seas, Ease after War.
Death after Life doth greatly please.'

THESE LINES FROM THE FIRST BOOK OF EDMUND SPENSER'S
The Faerie Queene open the 1940 diary. They must have
spoken to Ida at that moment, with Kenneth out on
stormy seas, the prospect of ease after war somewhere in an
uncertain future and death a very real possibility. The year
started bleakly: Kenneth was already seeing active service,
out on patrols on his ship in the Atlantic; Ida recorded
obsessively the news of each British ship that was torpedoed,
giving the numbers of officers and men dead or surviving;
and at home the weather was bitterly cold, with gales and
heavy snowfall, and the pipes froze at Elm Park Gardens,
leaving the family without running water for five weeks,
hauling water in pails from the hydrant in the street. Joan
moved up to Liverpool, where Kenneth's ship was based,
Hugh spent a lot of time shooting, Barbara was spending
every weekend in Chelmsford with her Hugh and Ida found
it difficult to distract herself from anxiety. Even a trip to the

theatre failed: Noel Coward's *Design for Living* seemed '*out of date and rather stupid*'.

The solution was to throw herself into work, and though her research team at the Lister was depleted, she pursued her interest in possible inhibitory factors in fats for developing tumours. She was working in collaboration with what she calls '*The Cancer Hospital*'; this will have been the Royal Marsden Hospital, then in the Fulham Road, founded in 1850 as the Free Cancer Hospital. Leslie Nunn was still working with her, though he would be moving on before long, and Margot Hume, in Cambridge, who was interested in dietary deficiency, was also contributing to the work. Ida was investigating the possible link between the development of tumours and deficiency in specific dietary fats. We are so used now to the idea that reducing fat makes for a healthy diet that it is easy to forget that fats are an essential component of a healthy diet, and Ida and her contemporaries were well aware of the effects of dietary deficiency in the depression of the 1930s.

While Ida was busy at the lab, domestic arrangements were difficult. With women being called on for war work, she no longer had a full domestic staff – in fact, Suzanne is the only person she mentions. She was chiefly the cook, though she probably did some other work. Ida liked her, but she was clearly not a very resourceful woman and was driven to distraction by the water problem. She also caused Hugh to be in a bad mood for days by asking him to phone the fishmonger:

'*Very busy at lab. Fishmonger didn't send fish for lunch – Suzanne completely overthrown – says it makes her a bunch of nerves – couldn't telephone. Went to H who phoned but made a great fuss. Told Suzanne she must not go to Hugh as he does not want to be troubled – (& he*

makes everything such a fuss). Must get someone in the
kitchen who can deal with things in my absence.'

She did not find anyone who could 'deal with things' and
Suzanne stayed until later in the year when the air raids
started and became too much for her. Hugh, as far as we know,
had never opposed Ida's working, but he still expected her to
take complete responsibility for domestic arrangements. Ida
did the best she could, but she was short of domestic skills;
she had grown up in a house full of servants and spent her
early adulthood in her mother's well-run house, where she was
not expected to take any responsibility. It amused me to note
that whenever she was called on to cook a meal, she invariably
fried sausages, and when Kenneth came home on leave and
Suzanne was out for the evening, it took the combined efforts
of Joan, Barbara and Ida to cook pork chops for dinner.

At the end of January, with Hugh in bed with severe
bronchitis and the house still waterless, bad news came from
Pinnock: Thoroughgood, their gardener and handyman,
reported that a beam had caught fire in the dining room
chimney and had blazed for twenty-four hours. Pinnock was
an unappealing prospect in the current weather conditions,
but Ida had plans for starting a poultry farm there. A lot of
people were keeping chickens to supplement wartime rations,
but Ida, of course, planned to do it on a grand scale – not just
a few hens to keep the family supplied with eggs but an initial
purchase of a hundred chicks. The fortunes of the hens would
often dominate Ida's diaries in the next two years.

In February, Ida dragged herself down to Pinnock after a
bout of flu and started making plans not only for the poultry
but for large-scale planting of vegetables. Thoroughgood was
to take charge, with his wife and daughter, who would also
manage the hens.

Back in the lab, she learnt that Leslie Nunn had been offered a research post in Runcorn, the centre of the chemical industry, and they were instructed to start preparing their lab for the effects of bomb blasts, covering glass-fronted cabinets with strips of gummed paper, and storing glassware securely.

At the beginning of March, Kenneth had his first battle injuries to treat – up until then, although they had been out on patrol, they had escaped attack and he had been treating minor illness among the men, and working on coding and decoding:

> 'The Walpole had been rescuing people from a gig steamer mined on the West Coast & Ken had had lots of burns & broken legs & other casualties. He'd only 1 night on shore & went out again on Sunday.'

At the same time, Hugh Beech was offered a research post with the Air Ministry. Barbara had told her parents that she would delay getting engaged until she knew what he intended to do in the war. It seems that he made the wrong decision as far as she was concerned. She went on seeing him for a few weeks – 'Barbara to Chelmsford as usual' – but then there is no further mention of him at all in Ida's diary. Barbara's memoir gives his decision not to join the armed forces as the main reason for ending the relationship, but she told Kenneth's children that her mother's opposition to the marriage was the main reason. Ida herself wrote nothing about any of this, nor does her diary suggest that Barbara was unhappy or unsettled at this time, though she was usually very much attuned to Barbara's moods. Barbara is mentioned often, but usually in terms of her job as a research assistant at the Ministry of Economic Warfare. It may be that Barbara's pride held her back from talking about her decision; having made such a scene about the engagement three months before, she may not have wanted to admit that her parents might have been right about Hugh's being, in her mother's view, 'not a serious person'. Barbara's disappointment at Hugh's decision may of course have coincided with Ida's disapproval in that both of them were experiencing daily anxiety, not only about Kenneth's danger, but about that of Oliver, in the paratroops. In a letter to Ida around this time, Joan wrote:

> 'I am so proud of our darling Ken, the way he has tackled things, because it is such a very different sort of life to what he had planned.'

Hugh's decision must have felt particularly unheroic by contrast.

Ida was working furiously, sometimes not even stopping for lunch – unheard of in the diaries, where the days are punctuated by reference to meals. At the beginning of March, she had sent off three papers on the effects of arachidonic acid to the *Biochemical Journal,* and she was getting a good deal of encouragement from scientists she respected to continue her work on tumours: from Nobel Prize-winner Arthur Harden and from future Nobel laureate Robert Robinson in Oxford. She subsequently withdrew one of the papers, but two were published in June in the *Biochemical Journal.*[38]

April was taken up with work and with setting up the poultry farm, but by May the war news was alarming: '*Today Holland and Sweden*', she wrote on 15th May, as though

---

38 *Biochemical Journal* 'Fat-deficiency disease of rats. The effect of doses of methyl arachidonate and lineolate on fat metabolism with a note on the estimation of arachidonic acid.' by Ida Smedley-MacLean, Leslie Charles Alfred Nunn, June 01 1940

• *Biochemical Journal* 'The synthesis of phospholipin in rats fed on the fat-deficient diet' by G.C. Hevesy, Ida Smedley-MacLean, June 01 1940.

surrenders were daily occurrences, and she made arrangements for the large hall at Crosby Hall to be handed over to the local council for use as a depot for clothing for Dutch and Belgian refugees. As the situation of the British Expeditionary Force in France became critical and the King made a broadcast to the British public, Ida – critical as she was of poor public speakers – gave the stammering King her seal of approval: '*Delivery much improved*'.

Enclosed in the pages for June is a printed letter from the Ministry of Information, signed by the Minister Duff Cooper:

> '*A great danger exists at the present time of loose talk and of loose thinking about what might be the consequences of defeat… It is therefore most important that people of influence such as yourself should do all in your power to fight against such dangerous opinions… This war is really a religious war, a war of right against wrong.*'

There is also a one-page leaflet: '*First Aid. Keep this in your pocket or bag.*' Ida started to take First Aid classes. On 25th June, they experienced their first air raid and slept in the '*Refuge Room*' in the basement. The next day, Ida took all her aluminium saucepans and cooking utensils to Chelsea Town Hall to be melted down for aeroplane manufacture, and heard that she had passed her First Aid exam with eighty-five per cent (she was always good at exams). Sir John Ledingham required all staff at the Lister to have tetanus and typhoid inoculations.

As the Blitz continued, Ida received a letter from Alice Parsons, her hostess on her trip to the US in 1919, which conveys how perilous the UK's situation looked from outside:

> '*Hadlyme, Conn. 14 July '40: Dear Ida, My hilltop is so beautiful this bright morning and so peaceful, that I'd like*

*to share it with you and yours. Can I be of any help?. –
If you'd want to send Barbara overseas for a while... I
believe that England will win through... and we think of
our friends constantly...'*

Pinnock at weekends offered some respite from the bombing,
but it was hard work. Thoroughgood had been taken ill and
admitted to hospital, and Hugh and Ida had to start harvesting
the vegetables being produced in industrial quantities.

In August, Hugh went for his annual holiday in Scotland,
war or no war. (He was so determined to ignore the war that
he forgot that there would be no restaurant car on the train,
and had to travel hungry to Inverness with only a couple of
chocolate bars that Ida managed to buy for him at the station.)
While he was away and writing home with holiday news of
walks and grouse, Ida was working furiously at the lab – 'No-
one else in the Institute' – lifting potatoes and moving fowl
houses at Pinnock; calming Suzanne, who was panicked by
ration books; and taking in neighbours to sleep in the Refuge
Room as the Blitz continued. She also suffered a severe
reaction from her obligatory typhoid inoculation.

At the beginning of September, news came from Pinnock
that Thoroughgood had died after surgery and Hugh returned
home. The air raids were now relentless; the family slept in
the Refuge Room with any neighbours who needed to join
them, but even in these circumstances, and in Ida's relaxed
household, class divisions operated – Suzanne slept not in the
Refuge Room but in the basement corridor, *'praying hard all
night'*, as well she might. She decided that sleeping at a nearby
shelter was a better option, and Barbara moved out to stay
with friends in Hampstead, further from the centre of the city.

Then, on 20th September, while Ida and Hugh were out
for the evening with Oliver, a bomb landed in their back

garden, smashing most of their windows and doing some structural damage. Suzanne departed to stay with a friend in Brighton, and Ida and Hugh were invited to stay with Olive in St Albans. For a few weeks, they commuted between St Alban's and work in London, making train journeys that often took three hours in wartime conditions. Ida knew that she was lucky to have refuge with Olive, but the travelling and the weekends of heavy work at Pinnock in the absence of a farm manager was exhausting her and she was enormously relieved in mid-October when her network of women colleagues came to her rescue. She had a letter from Marjory Stephenson offering the possibility of a lab in Cambridge. Stephenson was a woman Ida admired and respected. She was a bacterial biochemist working in Gowland-Hopkins's lab, and was one of the first two women to be elected Fellows of the Royal Society, but her route into an academic career had not been an easy one. She studied natural sciences at Newnham a decade later than Ida, and intended to go on to study medicine but did not have the funds to support herself; instead she became a domestic science teacher, quickly moving on to a lectureship at King's College of Household Science. There she was spotted by Robert Plimmer, one of the founders of the Biochemical Society, who invited her to join his lab at University College London, where she worked on fat metabolism and was awarded a Beit Memorial Research Fellowship three years after Ida was awarded hers. During the 1914–18 war, she ran hospital kitchens for the Red Cross in France, and was mentioned in dispatches and awarded an MBE at the end of the war, but her wartime experience turned her into a lifelong pacifist and she was a leading member of the Cambridge Scientists Anti-War Group.

On hearing from her, Ida went to Cambridge:

'Tues 15 Oct 1940

A very successful day at Cambridge. Saw Marjory Stephenson who sent me to Keilin [David Keilin, Director of the Molteno Institute] who has offered me a very nice room in the Molteno Institute.[39] Then lunched with Margot Hume at the K.P. Found Beatrice on her birthday feeling ill – she sent me to see Anna Pane's house which is to let furnished – altogether a good day – home to St Albans.'

So there was Marjory Stephenson to pull strings at the university and find her a lab, Beatrice Thomas to find her a place to live, and Margot Hume to work with. It was certainly a good day, and not undeserved – Ida had been doing this sort of thing for other women throughout her career.

On 3rd November, she and Hugh moved into their lodgings in Cambridge – not the house that Beatrice had found, in fact, but two furnished rooms in Bridge Street, in the city centre. Ida, I imagine, did not want another house to run without servants; in their furnished lodgings, their landlady would clean and cook for them and Ida could concentrate on her work. A lorry arrived with all her equipment to be unpacked into her new lab, with two staff from the Lister.

Ida was happy in Cambridge. Hugh went down to London regularly to see patients while she enjoyed her work – *'The rats are doing well'* – and a social and cultural life built around a few friends and the concerts, theatre and ballet that the city offered. She was free of domesticity and, always ready to enjoy her food, she decided to try out every restaurant and café in Cambridge for lunch. Kenneth sent cheerful, reassuring letters, and Barbara was happy with her work and friends.

---

39 The Molteno Institute was devoted to research in parasitology, but these were wartime conditions.

They had not yet found a new manager for Pinnock, but there was less to do during the winter months.

At the beginning of December, Kenneth was home on leave, he and Joan came up to Cambridge, and he was awarded his MA degree. An MA is not a postgraduate degree at Cambridge – anyone with a Cambridge BA has the right to become an MA, and thereby have the right to vote in university elections and borrow books from the university library. Two weeks before Kenneth took his MA, Ida had taken her own MA – more than forty years after she was denied the right to graduate with a BA. She celebrated by going to the library and taking a book out. It was a moment that had been a long time coming, and Kenneth's taking his MA added to the pleasure:

> 'Ken & I celebrating that we had taken the Master of Arts degree within a fortnight of each other – I think a record for mother and son.'

As Christmas approached, Billy, as usual, got in touch, but he was by now in what seems to be quite a desperate state – homeless and jobless, apparently:

> '7.12.40: Dear Di, I wrote to Linden Gardens to enquire if any letters… & received your card… You had still better send to that address as my movements have no certainty whatsoever… Do you ever come up to town? I should so like to see you. Things have not been good with me… Got a job & then turned it down because the pay was so poor. Now I much regret I did not take it. However if I were not to continually make mistakes, it just would not be me… love from Bill.'

There was no family Christmas supper party to invite him

to this year, but Ida met him in London and took him out for lunch before she and Hugh went down to Pinnock to spend a quiet Christmas with Barbara. She was happy to be with them – her letters to Ida in Cambridge made it clear that she was missing her mother very much – but it was hardly a cheerful Christmas, given Kenneth's absence and the state of the house, and the poultry, which had been being underfed. Encouraged by a three-day break in the bombing over Christmas, they stayed at Elm Park Gardens for a night, where they encountered renewed bombing, but she received a welcome phone call:

> 'During the Blitz Dr Weizmann rang up, they had just seen Michael off back to the North of Ireland where he is leader of a squadron bomber coastal command & they were feeling depressed & talking about old friends & felt they must ring up & find out where we were. So we arranged to lunch with them at the Dorchester tomorrow.'

The reunion was a delight, and a reminder of the earlier war, in which Ida had had an active part to play and the camaraderie of colleagues working on a vital project:

> 'I found W exactly as he was 20 years ago & full of plans for Substitute fuel from his bug[40] & heard all his efforts to get in touch with the various ministries – so like the old days – an interesting talk with Lord Lloyd who said to him Arabs meant oil – which W said he could produce. Enjoyed myself very much & promised to stay with them in Palestine & lecture at the University of Jerusalem!'

---

40 Weizmann, conscious of the power that oil exerted in the Middle East, was working on the production of aviation fuel and other oil products from fermented carbohydrate.

Ida and Hugh returned to Cambridge for the New Year, but she did not settle back into the brief tranquillity of November and December. Instead there was a restless shuttling between Cambridge, London and Gloucestershire. (Ironically, their Cambridge landlady, Mrs Jones, announced that she would like to discontinue cooking an evening meal for them as she did not want them to get *'too settled'*; she need not have worried – they could hardly have been more unsettled.) In early January, they were back down in London and found that a pipe had burst at Elm Park Gardens and water was coursing through Hugh's bedroom and the library, where books were ruined. Phoning an agency for a plumber, Ida was told that they could not guarantee to find one *'in days or weeks'*. They turned off the mains water, rescued the books as best they could and went back to Cambridge.

Two weeks later, they went to Pinnock and found that too in a dire state: the Thoroughgoods, mother and daughter, were not coping: the house was cold and dirty and the fowls *'in a shocking state'*. They slept on mattresses on the floor downstairs and both went down with flu, returning to Cambridge to spend a week in bed. The couple Ida found to replace the Thoroughgoods – a brother and sister – proved no more satisfactory: they sold the eggs and vegetables and pocketed the money, and the brother turned out to be *'a completely hopeless person… very insolent and utterly incapable of looking after anything'*.

Soon, however, concerns about burst pipes and hens were swept aside by the news from Max Armfield that Connie was seriously ill. Increasingly disabled and refusing medical treatment, she had developed severe bedsores, which had become septic and gangrenous. Ida and Hugh found her in agony, and Hugh insisted on bringing in a doctor and nurses to treat the sores. It was too late, however, and though she lingered in great pain for some time, she died in early March. Ida was very upset by the funeral and found Hugh less sympathetic than he had been at her father's funeral, rushing her away afterwards to get back to London in a way she found *'rather horrid'*. She was more distressed by Connie's death than she had been by her father's, perhaps because of the distance that had grown between them in recent years. They had, as she wrote, been *'unsympathetic to one another'*, unlike in their beliefs, attitudes and concerns, and Connie's relentless self-obsession must, in the end, have been a barrier to closeness. Ida supported Connie's and Max's often doomed artistic projects both financially and practically – the diaries are full of flyers and programmes for these enterprises – but Connie showed little interest in Ida or her family. The last letter from Connie, in 1940, is full of an entertainment she was putting on to celebrate the centenary of the wedding of Victoria and Albert, without a word of concern for Kenneth or mention of the war at all. But they had been so close as children, and Ida found that only her friend Beatrice, who had known them both at school, could understand how she was feeling:

> *'Beatrice seems to belong to the old life and to understand the break that Connie's death makes.'*

Billy, on the other hand, was less of a concern than he had been. Wartime brought out the best in him; his charm and affability were valuable commodities and, with lives at stake, he seems to have managed a reliability that had evaded him before:

> *'...then met Billy and had coffee with him at the Brasserie – found him really enjoying his work as a Kensington A.R.P. warden. His post had tackled 39 fires at the last*

big blitz on a March Saturday night. The other wardens were charming to him, he'd made friends with the portrait painter Gunn – altogether he was very happy to have regular occupation – & money.'

He was not rehabilitated as far as his wife and children were concerned, however; when his daughter, 'Peter', married in St Albans Cathedral later in the year, it was Oliver again, in the uniform of a captain in the paratroopers, who gave his sister away.

By July, arriving at Pinnock to find disarray – sick hens and mice in the larder and the linen cupboard – and after a *'stormy interview'* with their manager, they acknowledged that the poultry project was doomed and decided to cut their losses. They arranged to sell the hens and generate some income by letting the cottage out for a year from September onwards. Kenneth, writing from his ship, was sad to hear of their leaving Pinnock, which had become, in his mind, in the heat of the tropics, his ideal piece of England. His letters took up to a month to arrive and were heavily censored. They continued to be cheerful and reassuring: he was now doing some *'real medicine'* and was *'quite safe'*. Then, in September, Joan (living in Bradford with her mother and nursing at the Bradford Royal Infirmary) sent Ida a telegram:

'Ken Nursing home Colombo Bronchitis'.

This was followed by another telegram a week later:

'Ken recovered fortnight leave Whitegalle Face Hotel Colombo'.

Eventually, a letter came from Kenneth himself, written in his usual reassuring tone:

*'21/9/41, Fraser Nursing Home, Colombo, Ceylon.
"...I've been sent here to convalesce from an attack of
bronchitis or mild broncho-pneumonia... This is a first
class nursing home... I've got a very good R.N.V.R.
Doctor...".*

The full story would not emerge until later: Kenneth had in
fact been dangerously ill with bronchial pneumonia. Too ill to
diagnose and treat himself, he had been wrongly diagnosed
with malaria and treated on board ship with quinine for five
days before they docked in Colombo (in Ceylon, now Sri
Lanka) and he could start the right treatment.

By contrast with Kenneth's determinedly upbeat tone,
Barbara's letters to her mother were plaintive: she had been
sent to a ministry outpost in Warwick, where she had very
little to do, was desperately bored, missed her London life and
missed her parents – *'I don't like being an orphan at all.'*

At the end of September, Ida heard that a bomb had fallen
in the street where Beatrice Thomas lived. She hurried there
and found that a small bomb had landed on the pavement
outside Beatrice's house. She found Beatrice unhurt but badly
shaken – she had spent all night alone in the dark in her
house, which was a mass of broken glass, plaster and rubble.
Ida spent the following days looking after her.

Thwarted of the opportunity to give the parties she had
always enjoyed organising, she decided to give a tea party at the
lab in early November to celebrate the first year anniversary of
working there, and Ida and Hugh seem to have won over their
landlady, Mrs Jones, who was apparently reconciled to their
becoming *'settled'* in her house and presented them with an
iced cake to celebrate their year's occupation – quite a gesture
with butter and sugar precious commodities.

The year ended with a quiet Christmas back at Elm

Park Gardens with Barbara, and with Billy as usual for Christmas Day supper, but what tranquillity they could find was disturbed by a telegram to Hugh at the start of the New Year from Annie, his sister-in-law, letting him know that his nephew, Alistair, was missing in action. He had been on HMS *Audacious* protecting an Atlantic convoy, they had been engaged in a five-day battle and the *Audacious* had been sunk. He was posted as *'missing presumed killed'* at the beginning of February and Annie was admitted to a nursing home with a breakdown. Three weeks later, they heard that Annie was dead:

> *'When Hugh returned tonight he heard from Andrew that Annie had left the nursing home & her body had been found near the islands in the Ness. She was buried today. She is released from her misery – and no one could wish her back but it is terrible to die like this.'*

When Ida recorded Alistair's death in her diary, she added, *'No news of Ken'*. They did in fact have news of a sort, but not encouraging news:

> *'The news today is the Singapore causeway is blown up & the siege or attack is now on & Ken must be somewhere in that region.'*

She dealt with her anxiety by working even harder; she started to write her book – the definitive work on fats, entitled simply *The Metabolism of Fat*, a distillation of a lifetime's research. Having made the decision to write, she sent the first chapter to Methuen in March and was invited to see an editor there in early April. She found that Methuen no longer had a science editor and her book was being dealt with by a Mr

Rieu – E.V. Rieu, a classicist best known for his translations of Homer (his translation of the *Odyssey* was the first book to be published by Penguin Classics after the war). He had not read her chapter, and would not have understood it, but had consulted *'one or two friends'*, who had told her that Ida was 'It', and he had better publish her. It was hardly peer reviewing as we understand it, but the general view that Ida was 'It' was sound enough.

By that time, there was the best possible news of Kenneth: a phone call came from Joan in the middle of the night to tell them that he was coming home on leave. He arrived in March and, to Ida's and Joan's delight, was sent to Scotland, to work in the hospital on the naval base at Invergordon. Joan went with him, and in April they wrote to let Ida know that Joan was pregnant.

Perhaps it is this personal happiness and the prospect of a grandchild that accounts for a definite shift in focus in the 1942 diary. The earlier wartime diaries focus on getting through, on dealing with blackout and air raids, with rations and the absence of domestic help, with making Pinnock a wartime asset and Cambridge a place of work. The 1942 diary looks to the future in all sorts of ways. The phrases *'after the war'* and *'when the war is over'* crop up time and again, in plans for Crosby Hall, in a proposal to set up a residential club for women research workers, in plans for the long-term future of refugees, and in plans for their personal future: Kenneth's career ambitions, his and Joan's family life, the future of Pinnock, the idea of converting 2 Elm Park Gardens into flats.

In the early part of the year, the progress of the war was hardly encouraging enough for this hopeful forward planning: the attack on the American navy at Pearl Harbor at the end of 1941 had brought the USA into the war, but the Japanese were dominating the Far East and the fall of Singapore was a huge blow; the Germans had penetrated into Russia and Rommel was routing the allies in the Middle East ('*Sunday 29th. Returned to Cambridge. Last night the King broadcast asking for a day of prayer. Does this mean Hitler's Middle East offensive begins this week?*'). In April, the German 'Baedeker' air raids started, targeting Britain's historic towns and cities. It was not until the middle of the year that the tide seemed to be turning, with the defeat of German forces at El-Alamein in July, followed by further successes against Rommel's army, and the news, in the autumn, that the epic struggle for Stalingrad in the Soviet Union was going the Soviets' way, with German forces surrounded and starved of supplies. So, looking forward was something of an act of faith at the beginning of the year, but by the end of the year the sense that '*after the war*' was a time within reach, was possible.

In June, there was a lull in the bombing on London, and Ida and Hugh were confident enough to return to Elm Park Gardens. Ida had her sixty-fifth birthday and was obliged to retire from the Lister but received a gracious letter from the board awarding her a gratuity of six months' salary and assuring her of lab space for as long as she wanted it.

Ida made full use of the offer, continuing to work as before, and she also now had full responsibility for running the house. A Mrs Bull came in to do some cleaning, but Ida took over the cooking (Kenneth and Joan sent her a birthday present of a Pyrex dish, which they hoped would be '*useful in your housekeeping adventures*'. She took to the cooking with enthusiasm, though some of her wartime improvisations sound a little odd – lettuce and macaroni soup, for example! She was pleased with her progress and by the middle of July she could write '*Cooked dinner very successfully. Getting quicker and much improving*'. By then, she had also restored the house to rights, including the books in the damaged library, and had typed up the final chapter of her book. With a 1st September deadline in mind, she was driving herself to complete her manuscript before 10th August, when they were due to travel up to Invergordon to spend time with Kenneth and Joan. She did it, sending the manuscript in on her return from Scotland in time to make preparations for a return visit from Joan and Kenneth, who now had two weeks' leave.

Her accounts of these weeks, first in Scotland and then in London – delighting in the time spent with her family, making plans, anticipating the baby, buying a pram at the Army and Navy Stores – are some of the happiest in the diaries, even though war news was never far away.

In October, with the book at Methuen, Joan and Kenneth back in Scotland, the First Aid certificate achieved, and the house and cooking under control, she was looking for something more to do, so she contacted the Ministry of Food to offer her expertise in dietary deficiency to decisions to be made about food rationing. The civil servant who interviewed her was *terribly respectful* but was clearly flummoxed as to how to deal with someone of such eminence. Her offer was politely declined.

Then, in November, came the news of the birth of Anthony Hugh (with an entertaining letter from Kenneth describing how the two of them – a nurse and a doctor – took twenty minutes to decide whether Joan, with lower abdominal pains, was in labour!). Ida was as absurd as any other first-time grandmother – *'Everyone has to hear about Anthony Hugh'* – and was delighted to listen to him crying on the other end of the phone.

Shades of trouble to come are there, though, in her last diary entry of the year:

> *'Very lame with neuritis in R leg & no domestic help from Friday to Monday after Mrs Bull had cooked the Xmas dinner.'*

Sciatica had been her constant companion for at least ten years, but she was usually able to rise above it. This time it seems to have exhausted her, and the diary ends without any of her usual reflections on what had passed or anticipation of what was to come.

CHAPTER FOURTEEN

NEVER FAILED TO INSPIRE

1943 and Beyond

No diary has survived for 1943. Barbara writes that Ida was bedridden with what was initially diagnosed as 'neuritis' for most of that year, and that X-rays eventually showed that the pain was being caused by a cancer which had spread to her bones. She was in extreme pain for much of that year and died in University College Hospital on 2nd March the following year. Her friend Martha Whiteley rather challenged Barbara's recollection of her being bedridden for a year, writing in her obituary that she had continued working in her lab at the Lister until a few months before her death. This sounds more like the Ida I came to know. Certainly, she must have worked on correcting the proofs of her book, which came out that spring, and she published her final paper[41] in the *Biochemical Journal* in April. As another of her obituarists wrote, '*She achieved everything she set out to do.*'

But she did not see Anthony Hugh grow up, nor his sister, Anne, born three years later, and she was not able to help Hugh when he fell down the basement steps in the blackout at Elm

---

41 *Biochemical Journal* 'The structure of arachidonic and linoleic acids' by C.L. Arcus, Ida Smedley-MacLean, April 01 1943.

Park Gardens in 1943 and fractured his skull. He recovered physically but slipped back into a deep depression from which he never emerged. '*The death of his wife the following year may well have weighed the scales against him*', Kenneth wrote in his obituary. Hugh lived on, in a nursing home, until his death at the age of seventy-eight.

For Barbara, who had regarded wartime separation from her parents as '*being an orphan*', the reality of losing both parents, especially her mother, on whom she was so dependent, must have been very hard. And she suffered a further loss: the man she was going to marry was killed in action and she never married. She stayed in the Civil Service, became its youngest Principal and subsequently worked as a Senior Advisor to the Atomic Energy Authority, playing a significant role in negotiations when the UK joined the EU.

Kenneth survived the war and was able to pick up his medical career and lead a long and fulfilling life, becoming Consultant Physician at Guy's Hospital, where he had trained.

The many obituaries of Ida written by her women colleagues express genuine grief for her loss and admiration for her achievements, but the one that perhaps most vividly conveys both her intellectual and her personal qualities is that written in *Nature* by a man – her long-time student and co-researcher, Leslie Nunn. It is a beautifully written piece, which deftly summarises her scientific work and concludes with the following tribute:

> '*Much has been omitted in this brief note but it is hoped that sufficient has been said to indicate the late Dr Smedley-MacLean's comprehensive and intense interest in the biochemistry of fat. I worked with her for many years and I retain the sense and knowledge of her masterly grip of her field. She sought out the facts, made sure of*

them, and then held to them amid much cross-fire. She saw the significant correlations between her facts very clearly and rarely went beyond. As a teacher and colleague she never failed to inspire and there must be many like myself who look back on their "Lister" days with intensely happy memories.'

'Masterly' is the word he uses to describe her, and mastery is what she sought. I give the last word to Ida herself, in the speech she gave in 1927 at a Lyceum Club debate, at the height of her own personal happiness and professional success:

'Is it the woman who is utterly dependent for her happiness on her personal relationships who at the end of her life can look back and say "My life has been happy" or is it the woman who as far as possible makes a life of her own on which she depends for happiness? To this her personal relationships may bring great added joys, but if they fail her altogether, if they bring much sorrow instead of happiness into her life, her life is still not shipwrecked for she has still something of which she is master.'

APPENDIX I

Obituary

Dr Ida Smedley-MacLean
Nature vol 154 22nd July 1944
Leslie C.A. Nunn

After graduation... Dr MacLean (then Miss Ida Smedley)
worked on certain problems of pure organic chemistry under
Prof. H.R. Armstrong, investigating *inter alia* the cause of
colour in the dinitrobenzenes. She also acted as demonstrator in
Chemistry and carried out researches on problems concerning
the increase in molecular refractivity of compounds containing
a conjugated ethenoid linkage structure. The work resulted in
a very interesting communication on the diphenylbutadienes
and hexatrienes published in the *Journal of the Chemical
Society* 1908. Shortly after this early work, Miss Smedley was
awarded a Beit Memorial Research Fellowship and went to
work in the biochemical laboratories of the Lister Institute,
under Arthur Harden, chemist-in-chief... One must suppose
that about this time Miss Smedley developed the intense
and lifelong interest in problems of fat metabolism. Study
of fat metabolism and fat synthesis had already been actively
pursued at the Institute... it was however a field in which
few then delved. Dr Hugh MacLean, who later took a great

interest in the study of the lipins, arrived at the Institute as one of Hardens assistants at about the same time as Miss Smedley, and their marriage took place in 1913.

Dr Smedley-MacLean perceived early the biochemical significance and importance of fats. Though today much is obscure in our knowledge of fats, her work has made a valuable contribution to our knowledge of the subject and particularly to those parts of it which deal with the oxidative breakdown of fatty acids *in vitro* and their synthesis by living organisms. Her early investigations in this field led to the deduction of the presence of a decyclenic acid in butter fat, a deduction confirmed by isolation at the hands of other workers some years later. In 1912 there appeared two papers in the *Biochemical Journal* the possible mode of synthesis *in vivo*, in collaboration with Eva Lubrzynska. Laboratory experiments on the condensation together of such simple compounds as aldehydes and pyruvic acid led to the isolation of longer carbon chain substances of a fatty nature. The work crystallized itself in the hypothesis that pyruvic acid was a very probable starting point for the synthesis of fatty acid in the body. It is a hypothesis that merits to this day a most serious consideration by students of this subject. Even now we do not know the actual steps by which fatty acids are built up from carbohydrates *in vivo*. Of added interest and significance in this connexion are the later investigations of other workers on the importance of pyruvic acid on carbohydrate transformations.

With the war of 1914–1918, Dr Smedley-MacLean's energies were diverted to other pressing problems. With Dr Chaim Weizmann, she worked on the problems of producing acetone on the large scale from starch fermentation, a project that was eminently successful. After the war, and in spite of greatly increased domestic responsibilities, Dr Smedley-MacLean threw herself with great energy into the well-loved work, and many important and interesting papers on the mode of synthesis of fat and carbohydrate in yeast appeared at intervals until about 1939. While seeking a possible laboratory model for the study of the biochemical oxidation of fatty acids, she discovered that hydrogen peroxide in the presence of a cupric salt as catalyst is extraordinarily powerful in its oxidizing action on fatty acids. In a short time the higher fatty acids may be largely broken down to carbon dioxide, a chemical transformation very difficult or impossible to perform in any other way. This field she cultivated with some success up to some weeks before her death.

From about 1935 onwards, interest centred on the fat-deficiency disease of rats discovered by Burr and Burr in 1929 (*J. Biol. Chem.* 82, 346; 1929). At the Lister Institute the physiological aspects were more closely studied in conjunction with Miss Hume and Miss Henderson-Smith, while the biochemical side was left to Dr Smedley-MacLean and myself. Her delight and fascination with this work never left her. Besides many other interesting and significant points uncovered, the position of linoleic acid as the probable precursor of arachidonic acid and other very unsaturated acids was established. The nature of the fatty acids stored under conditions of disease and cure was also investigated. Finally the structure of arachidonic acid itself... was put forward as a result of investigation on a very small quantity of material. The suggested structure was fully confirmed by subsequent work with large quantities in the United States.

Much has been omitted in this brief note but it is hoped that sufficient has been said to indicate the late Dr Smedley-MacLean's comprehensive and intense interest in the biochemistry of fat. I worked with her for many years and I retain the sense and knowledge of her masterly grip of her field. She sought out the facts, made sure of them, and then held to them amid much cross-fire. She saw the significant correlations between her facts very clearly and rarely went beyond. As a teacher and colleague she never failed to inspire and there must be many like myself who look back on their 'Lister' days with intensely happy memories.

APPENDIX II

Extract from a talk by Robert Freedman for ESHS, Prague, September 2016

Ida Smedley-MacLean (1877–1944): Pioneering Biochemist and Feminist Campaigner

Ida Smedley-MacLean was a long-time researcher at the Lister Institute in London, an acknowledged expert on the chemistry and biochemistry of fats. From the early 1930s onwards, she was doing complex feeding experiments on rats, showing that they have a specific requirement for dietary fat. She was on the trail of what we now call the 'essential fatty acids' and made key contributions to this field. She was also collecting material for a major monograph on fat metabolism (Smedley-MacLean, 1943) which was her final publication. And she was refining the analytical methods that would enable her to determine the structure of arachidonic acid, the most crucial and most complex essential fatty acid. She analysed the chemical structure of fatty acids in butter and other sources, showing that they were exclusively straight chains containing even numbers of carbon atoms (Smedley, 1912). And she also published an important theoretical paper (Smedley & Lubrzynska, 1913) proposing a mechanism by which fatty acids could be built up from smaller components derived from carbohydrates. She proposed a chemically plausible precursor (pyruvic acid) and a chemically plausible mechanism in which fatty acid chains were built up and elongated 2-carbon atoms at a time. This work gained her an international reputation (it was only forty years later, after her death, that this mechanism was finally confirmed and the nature of the carrier of the 2-carbon intermediate identified).

She was still active in research at the Lister in the late 1930s and this period led to her second key research achievement. Earlier work had established the basic nutritional needs of humans and other mammals and defined the key vitamins, including the vitamins A and D, which are present in animal fats. But rats fed on a defined diet lacking fats, but with plentiful calories and protein and supplemented with vitamins A and D, fail to thrive. This 'fat-deficiency disease' can be reversed by small doses of natural oils and fats. Ida investigated this through the 1930s in complex feeding experiments, refining the nature of the essential components absent from the fat-free diet and also analysing the small amounts of fat stored in these lean and fat-deprived animals (Hume et al., 1938; Nunn & Smedley-MacLean, 1938; Smedley-MacLean & Nunn, 1938). She identified two fatty acids (linoleic and linolenic acids) as the essential dietary fatty acids, and showed that these could be converted in vivo into the more complex 20 C polyunsaturated fatty acid, arachidonic acid, which is the precursor for some essential hormones, the prostaglandins. Finally, in a paper published in 1940, just when her laboratory was being evacuated from London to Cambridge to avoid bombing, she published the correct full structure for arachidonic acid and identified the positions of the double bonds in the carbon chain (Dolby et al., 1940). This work was recently celebrated in a review in the Journal of Lipid Research (Martin et al., 2016), which highlighted the small quantities of material that Ida and her collaborators had to work with, and the use of entirely traditional techniques, with no modern spectroscopy.

APPENDIX III

IDA SMEDLEY-MACLEAN'S
PAPERS IN THE *BIOCHEMICAL JOURNAL*

(formatted as in the Biochemical Society's online archive)

The Fatty Acids of Butter *Ida Smedley (Beit Memorial Fellow)* Biochemical Journal Jan 01 1912

The Biochemical Synthesis of the Fatty Acids *Ida Smedley, Eva Lubrzynska* Biochemical Journal Jul 01 1913

The Presence of Vitamin A in Yeast Fat *Ethel Marjorie Luce, Ida Smedley-MacLean* Biochemical Journal Jan 01 1925

The examination of yeast fat for the presence of vitamins A and D before irradiation and of vitamin D after irradiation *Eleanor Margaret Hume, Hannah Henderson Smith, Ida Smedley-MacLean* Biochemical Journal Jan 01 1928

The Oxidation of Oleic Acid by means of Hydrogen Peroxide *Ida Smedley-MacLean, Margaret Sarah Beavan Pearce* Biochemical Journal Jan 01 1931

The nature of the lipoid matter extracted from green leaves (spinach and cabbage) *Dorothy Louisa Collison, Ida Smedley-MacLean* Biochemical Journal Jan 01 1931

The influence of succinic, fumaric, malic and acetic acids on the deposition of liver-glycogen, *Annie Phyllis Ponsford, Ida Smedley-MacLean* Biochemical Journal Jan 01 1932

The oxidation of palmitic acid by means of hydrogen dioxide in the presence of a cupric salt, *Ida Smedley-MacLean and Margaret Beavan Pearce* Biochemical Journal Jan 1934

The oxidation of the fatty dibasic palmitic acids and of laevulic acid by hydrogen dioxide in presence of a cupric salt, *Annie Phyllis Ponsford, Ida Smedle-MacLean,* Biochemical Journal Jan 1934

Note on the storage of carbohydrate and fat by Saccharomyces Frohberg when incubated in sugar solutions, *Rachel Anne McAnally and Ida Smedle- MacLean* Biochemical Journal Jan 1934

The oxidation of the fatty acids in vitro with especial reference to the oxidation of β-hydroxybutyric acid and acetoacetic acids *Robert Owen Jones, Ida-Smedley MacLean* Biochemical Journal July 01 1935

The oxidation of phenyl derivatives of fatty acids with hydrogen peroxide in the presence of copper *Robert Owen Jones, Ida Smedley-MacLean* Biochemical Journal Aug 01 1935

The synthesis of reserve carbohydrate by yeast *Rachel Anne McAnally, Ida Smedley-MacLean* Biochemical Journal Aug 01 1935

The synthesis of carbohydrate by yeast II, *Rachel Anne McAnally, Ida Smedley M-cLean* Biochemical Journal Sept 01 1935

The oxidation products of the unsaturated acids of linseed oil *Leslie Charles Alfred Nunn, Ida Smedley-MacLean* Biochemical Journal De 01 1935

The synthesis of reserve carbohydrate by yeast, *Rachel Anne McAnally, Ida Smedley-MacLean,* Biochemical Journal Jan 01 1937

The carbohydrate and fat metabolism of yeast, *Leslie Dundonald Macleod, Ida Smedley-MacLean* Biochemical Journal Sep 01 1938

The nature of the fatty acids stored by the liver in the fat-deficiency disease of rats, *Leslie Charles Alfred Nunn, Ida Smedley-MacLean* Biochemical Journal Dec 01 1938

Studies of the essential unsaturated fatty acids in relation to the fat-deficiency disease of rats, *Eleanor Margaret Hume, Leslie Charles Alfred Nunn, Ida Smedley-MacLean, Hannah Henderson-Smith* Biochemical Journal Dec 01 1938

Fat-deficiency disease of rats. The effect of doses of methyl arachidonate and lineolate on fat metabolism with a note on the estimation of arachidonic acid. *Ida Smedley-MacLean, Leslie Charles Alfred Nunn* Biochemical Journal Jun 01 1940

The synthesis of phospholipin in rats fed on the fat-deficient diet *G.C. Hevesy, Ida Smedley-MacLean* Biochemical Journal Jun 01 1940

Fat-deficient diseases of rats. The relation of the essential unsaturated acids to tumour formation in the albino rat on normal diet. *Ida Smedley-MacLean, Leslie Charles Alfred Nunn* Biochemical Journal Sep 01 1941

Fat-deficiency disease of rats. The influence of tumour growth on the storage of fat and of polyunsaturated acids in the fat-starved rat. *Ida Smedley-MacLean, Eleanor Margaret Hume* Biochemical Journal 01 Sep 1941

Fat-deficiency disease of rats. The storage of fat in the fat-starved rat. *Ida Smedley-MacLean, Eleanor Margaret Hume* Biochemical Journal 01 Sep 1941

The structure of arachidonic and linoleic acids *C.L. Arcus, Ida Smedley-MacLean* Biochemical Journal Apr 01 1943

SELECTED BIBLIOGRAPHY

Cohen, S. 'Crossing borders: academic refugee women, education and the British Federation of University Women during the Nazi era', *Journal of the History of Education Society* vol 39 2010 – issue 2

Fara, P. *A Lab of One's Own: Science and Suffrage in the First World War* (Oxford: O.U.P. 2018)

MacLean, B. *Some Midland Ancestors* (unpublished, 1997)

Munk's Roll *Lives of the Physicians* (Royal College of Physicians)

Nunn, L.C.A. 'Dr Ida Smedley-MacLean', *Nature* Vol. 154 (July 1944)

Peck, W. *Ida Smedley Maclean: Cambridge, Women and Science in the First World War* (unpublished MA dissertation)

Rayner-Canham, M. and Rayner-Canham, G. *Chemistry Was Their Life* (London: Imperial College Press, 2008)

Sharpley, E. (transcribed by Archer Hind, L.) War *Work 1914-1918, Newnham College Cambridge* (Newnham College Archives)

Smedley, A.C. *Crusaders: Reminiscences* (London: Duckworth, 1929)

Sondheimer, J. *History of the British Federation of University Women, 1907–1957* (BFUW, 1957)

Tennyson, Hallam (ed.) *Alfred Lord Tennyson: A Memoir by His Son* (Whitefish Montana: Kessinger Publishing, 2010)

Weizmann, C. *Trial and Error* (1949)